Go Back To Nature & Heal your 'Self'

GURDIP HARI

**AUTHOR OF AWARD WINNING
'MENTAL, PHYSICAL & SPIRITUAL
HEALTH'**

**Jasmin Publishing House
Irvine, California, USA**

Also by Gurdip Hari

Light of Hope
ISBN 0-9766186-1-3
The Conscious, Unconscious & Super-Conscious Mind
ISBN 0-9766186-0-5
Mental, Physical & Spiritual Health
ISBN 0-9766186-5-6
Mental, Physical & Spiritual Health - Audio Book
ISBN 0-9766186-4-8

Cover design: Jamel Goodloe

Edited by my two daughters:
Alipt Sanam Hari and Jasmin Hari

Jasmin Publishing House,
18 Indiana, Irvine, CA 92606, USA
Email: Jasmin@jasminpublishing.com

Visit our Websites:
http://www.Jasminpublishing.com
http://www.Humanityandlove.com
http://www.Healthisultimatewealth.com
http://www.healthymindfm.com

Acknowledgments

Quote from 20,000 Days and Counting by
Robert D. Smith used with his kind permission

Quote from The Five-Talent Mentality by
Albert & Comfort Ocran used with their kind permission

Reference from Creative Schools by Ken Robinson
in my own words

Reference from Dying to Be Me by Anita Moorjani
in my own words

Reference from The Alchemist by Paulo Coelho
in my own words

Special Thanks

To my sweeter-half, Daljit, for being a strong and loving pillar of support in the six year journey that I undertook to Go Back to Nature and write this Book.

To the new daughter of our Family, Alipt Sanam Hari, for her input and edit to give more meaning to this work.

To my little Princess, Jasmin, who is now ready to become a Queen, for the extraordinary touches given to this work.

To my brother, Amardeep and my son, Sanam for their great support in helping me to carry on our Father's great work to greater heights.

To my good friend and nephew Jamel, for designing such thought-provoking and inspirational covers for my books.

Legal Disclaimer

Dedication

This Book is dedicated to my loving Father,
Who left for that place we call 'Heaven',
In March of the year two thousand,
And became 'My Guiding Light'.
All that I do and have done,
Since the day he physically left,
Has been through his guidance in 'Spirit'.
And that's what I call Love,
Or rather 'True Eternal Love',
Ever present and everywhere,
In each and every part of me.
And I dedicate this work to that Love,
Which is in you, in me, in all Creation,
And truly, we all are a part,
Of that Bigger part we call God or Nature,
Or our very own source of Creation.
And what better Name can we give,
To that Force,
If not Love, what will it be?

Preface

What a beautiful lovely morning,
Cool drops of warm summer rain,
Falling on my cold Heart's window pane,
Washing away the fears and failures of yesterday.
Every single day like this morning,
Is afresh and new,
So are our Hearts,
Always clear like the Morning dew.
The way Sun rises with warmth and radiance,
Let's rise with our dreams,
Put the fears and failures behind,
In the quest for Eternal wisdom.
Fears will turn into rain drops,
And wash away our failures,
With our inner Sunlight,
Its warmth and radiance.
A beautiful lovely morning,
Welcomes us every single day,
All we need to do,
Is to fall in Love with ourselves,
Again, Again, and Again.

Foreword

Who am I,
Am I a part of this Creation,
Or is the Creation part of Me?
Who am I,
Am I connected to you,
Or are you connected to Me?
Who am I,
Am I this physical body,
Or much more than my eyes can see?
Who am I,
Am I the song of Love,
Or does Love sing through Me?
Is it difficult to find out,
Who am I,
Have I travelled too far,
Am I lost in the wilderness,
Of my illusions and fascinations?
All the answers are within Me,
And to know who I am,
I got to take that return journey,
"Back to Nature".

Contents

Introduction   11

Chapter 1   Knowledge is Power   21

Chapter 2   It's all about Change   31

Chapter 3   Knowing your 'Self'   43

Chapter 4   The Truth will set you Free   59

Chapter 5   Go Back to Nature   77

Chapter 6   A New Way of Life   93

Chapter 7   How to Heal your Self   141

Introduction

Change is the real name of the game of life being enacted on planet Earth with our active or passive participation. Those who are not afraid of change become active players, and are responsible for the majority of progress taking place. While the others who fear change usually stick to the tried and tested ways, and their contribution toward progress is minimal. With the efforts of the doers and non-doers a lot has changed in the last one hundred years, and I will highlight the seven most noteworthy changes that have completely revolutionized the way we live now in comparison to yesteryears.

Hundred years ago, almost half of all the people in developed nations lived in households with six or more people, and now, they either live alone or with an unmarried partner.

Hundred years ago, life expectancy was fifty-three, whereas now this has risen to seventy-five years. Previously, the leading causes of death were pneumonia and influenza, and now the leading two main causes are cancer and heart disease.

Hundred years ago, there were more married couple households in developed nations, the United States in particular; these are now in a deep state of decline, as the number of one-person homes has increased more than homes of any other size.

Hundred years ago, people knew most of their neighbors on a first name basis and regularly communicated with them face to face. Now, the majorities hardly know who their neighbors are and communicate more over social media, with people they know or hardly know.

Hundred years ago, natural cures like Homeopathy, Ayurveda, and Naturopathy were extremely popular, thanks to their impressive successes in treating many of the epidemics of the nineteenth century. Now, prescription drugs and medications have taken over, which are extremely dangerous for the human body as they merely suppress the symptoms of the disease, but completely fail in treating the root cause.

Hundred years ago, Agriculture was pure, sustainable, free from poisonous pesticides and herbicides, which made the land and human beings more fertile with each passing year. Now, it is primarily profit driven and infested with impurities. With the use of GMO seeds and dangerous chemicals, not only the land, but also majority of the humankind has become corrupted, worn out, unproductive, and increasingly infertile with each passing year.

Hundred years ago, it was perhaps a dream to imagine human beings flying in the air. Now, we can fly all around the world within a matter of hours in the wonderful aircrafts that have been invented. A trip to the Moon was just an imagination, but now it has turned into a reality.

Although numerous other things have changed in the last hundred years, which have impacted our lives both positively as well negatively, let us briefly focus on these seven to find out if we are heading in the right direction.

The first change brings forth a stark reality that hundred years ago there was more family bonding, as six or more people lived together in a household. This further highlights another reality that the institute of marriage was far stronger than it is today, and children had a better upbringing and thus better moral values. The violent incidents and senseless killings, terrorism, drug abuse, and many other prevailing ills were rare. So are we heading in the right direction?

The second change highlights the fact that the average human age has increased, which means we are living longer. This could be considered a positive element, but although the average age may have increased, there are greater stress levels and lower health conditions. We may be living longer with the help of drugs and supplements that extend our lifespan, but how good is the quality of our health? So are we really heading in the right direction?

The third change confirms the grave condition of the institution of marriage in developed nations as compared to hundred years ago. If married couple households have declined, it certainly means marriages are in a state of decline as well. In fact, now more men and women prefer to remain single and have a no strings attached live-in relationship; and quite often children are born out of wedlock. In the United States, in particular, a growing number of children live with single parents due to the rampant divorce rate. Many siblings have different mothers or fathers, and a good number are being raised by grandparents or relatives. So are we heading in the right direction?

The fourth change brings forth the harsh truth about the ever-increasing communication gap taking place in societies, neighborhoods, and cities. People no longer care to know who the neighbors are or interact with them. It is not as if we are not communicating; as a matter of fact, we're communicating more than ever now. But instead of being face-to-face, we prefer to connect with each other through the impersonal means our modern high-tech gadgets have enabled us with. Even simple activities such as birthday wishes from family members living in the same household are now being relayed via internet. Have a look at the photograph on the adjoining page which appeared on the social media, titled, 'Visiting Grandma'. This picture truly depicts the reality of the on-going communication gap. As you can see, six members of a family are visiting Grandma on a holiday or maybe 'Thanksgiving', and all of them are sitting with their heads down, deeply engrossed in interacting with people on the internet, while the old lady is patiently waiting as to when they will have some conversation with her.

So are we really heading in the right direction?

The fifth change is about how the methods of healing have shifted. Hundred years ago natural cures played a major role in keeping us healthy and fit, as people had more faith in the words of 'Hippocrates – The Father of Medicine', who said it is not medicine, but Nature or the life-force within the human body which heals. Although the modern medical doctors take the Hippocratic Oath upon graduating, they hardly practice what he preached. Instead, they do the complete opposite by bombarding the human body with extremely harmful drugs and medications, leading to long-term complications and even more health problems. So are we really heading in the right direction?

Change number six is about Agriculture and the foods we consume. Hundred years ago the foods were pure and safe for consumption as they did not contain any poisonous pesticides, dangerous chemicals, and did not come from genetically modified seeds. The ancient way of organic agriculture not only made the land more fertile with each passing year, it also played a great role in keeping us healthy and productive. The daily intake of foods laden with life-threatening elements is one of the main reasons for the widespread increase in sickness and disease this last century has seen. Billions of dollars have been poured into cancer research, but there's no sign of a cure yet. If a fraction of that money had been spent to find the root cause of not only cancer, but every disease that strikes the human body, we could have easily found the cure. So are we really heading in the right direction?

Change number seven highlights and demonstrates the truth about how limitless and free from boundaries the 'Human Spirit' is. The word impossible ceases to exist and there is virtually nothing beyond the reach of the 'Spirit'. Setting foot on the Moon and freely flying around from one corner of the world to another in a matter of hours is enough evidence of the amazing powers it is clothed with. In fact, who has invented these space-crafts, cars, computers, cell-phones, television, and internet? Is it not the same 'Spirit' enshrined in the human body responsible for every single invention? If it is, then how important is the human body itself – the home of the Spirit on planet Earth?

In my previous book, 'Mental, Physical & Spiritual Health', I clearly outlined this truth through these words: "Mind is the driver, Body the vehicle, and Spirit – The Real you, is the passenger. He who understands this truth and begins to live according to the simple laws of Nature will gain freedom from ill-health and begin to enjoy the wonders of life and success in every field by becoming mentally, physically, and spiritually fit."

But then, what is the Truth? A number of spiritual personalities, philosophers, and learned men have emphasized the importance of understanding its true meaning. They have repeatedly stated that the truth is bitter, but when you truly taste that bitterness and realize the real meaning – you'll be set Free. The scriptures confirm another important reality that the Human Body is the actual Temple of God, and we are the priests or pastors responsible to keep it clean, healthy and holy. If you understand and realize the meaning and significance of these words, wouldn't you take your job as a priest or pastor more seriously?

It is important to understand your true Nature – The real you, which is the Spirit inside a human body. It is equally important to know how to take care of the Body you live in. Just like your physical home defines your status and state of mind, the same holds true for your 'Spiritual Home'. If your physical home is clean and foundationally strong, it will be free from all kinds of disease-causing germs and will stand tall if any natural disaster strikes. The same concept holds true for your spiritual home. The cleanliness will serve as the foundation to keep it free from disease-causing germs, and help you stand tall in any kind of crisis.

Why is it that six out of the seven most noteworthy changes of the last one hundred years seem to be negative, and why do we need to ask ourselves if we are heading in the right direction? Why is it that family bonding, marriage, and face-to-face communications have declined, while sickness and disease have abnormally increased due to a change in the ways of agriculture and healing methods? A clean body leads to a healthy state of mind, and that in turn leads to success in every area of your life.

Basically, to be able to do the amazing and miraculous things you are truly capable of, you must first fully understand who you really are. The purpose of this Book is to help you know your Self better, and show you how to take care of the physical body, which is your home on planet Earth. If this is what you truly want, then come take a journey with me 'Back to Nature'. A journey like none other you may have ever taken, and Heal your Self in every single aspect.

Chapter 1

Knowledge is Power

Knowledge is Power – This is a common phrase you may have heard several times during your school or college days.

It's true, Knowledge is Power, but only when practically applied, and then it can further transcend into wisdom. There are countless people in the world who have the basic knowledge that cleanliness is an essential aspect of everyday life. We all know how important it is to have a clean home, clean utensils, clean clothes, and a clean outer body. The majority of us do make a practical application of this to ensure cleanliness in these areas and enjoy the relevant benefits accordingly.

When does knowledge transcend into wisdom? You may have all the knowledge that exists in the universe about cleanliness, but it's absolutely useless if you don't make any practical application of it. You may continue to live in an unclean home, eat in unclean bowls, and wear unclean clothes; and that will become your way of life. You'll never know the difference, nor will you be able to enjoy the benefits of the knowledge about cleanliness, until you make a practical application. Once you do that repeatedly and see the results, it will metamorphose into wisdom; and wise people do live in clean homes, eat in clean bowls, wear clean clothes, and take a bath daily to keep their outer bodies clean.

Although, a number of wise people live in clean homes, the emphasis is on inner cleaning. Generally, the areas that are used more often, such as the kitchen, dining, and bathrooms, will be cleaned perhaps daily, and certainly more often than the rest. Where the outside is concerned, the cleaning of the garden area and pavements may normally be left for the gardener or done on a weekly or bi-weekly basis. The focus is definitely more on inner cleaning and the reasons are not hard to find. If you don't clean the kitchen, dining, and bathroom regularly, there could be an army of roaches, ants, and bacteria invading your home, resulting in unhygienic conditions, which almost always leads to sickness and disease.

Have you ever thought of your physical body as a home in which you live? A great number of philosophers and prophets of various religions spent a great deal of their lives getting to know themselves and the bodies they lived in. When they found out who they were, they utilized their remaining years in making practical applications of that knowledge to make others aware of the unique divine nature we possess as human beings. They also discovered some simple truths about the human body, and realized, it was the real Temple of God. If you can relate to this reality and consider your physical body as a temple or a home in which you live, then who are you really? Would that not make you a unique entity, and would you not consider yourself responsible for the outer as well inner cleansing of the physical home you inhabit?

The sad fact of our existence on earth is that the majority of us do not realize our true identity and the importance and need for inner cleanliness of the body we live in. Where the physical home made by man from bricks, stones, and cement is concerned, the need for inner cleanliness is well understood and practiced by most to avoid sickness, disease, and related discomfort. But for the other home made by God or Nature from flesh and blood, the importance of inner cleanliness is neither understood nor practiced by the multitude.

Have you ever wondered why sickness and disease are on the rise when trillions of dollars are being spent annually to find cures, and hospitals after hospitals are being built around the globe? The truth is indeed bitter, and the bitter truth is that no amount of money, doctors, or hospitals can be a substitute for inner cleanliness. If cracks keep on developing in a building due to a foundational fault, no amount of money on materials and labor can permanently fix them, until the basic fault is corrected. Year after year you may carry out repairs and spend billions into research to develop materials for a permanent fix, but they'll continue to reappear at different times in different formats. The same holds true where the modern medical establishment is concerned. They keep on building new hospitals, training more and more doctors, and spending endlessly into research and development of new materials known as drugs to find a permanent cure, but the cracks in the form of sickness and disease continue to reappear.

Once there was a King whose kingdom had a serious problem of flooding every time it rained heavily. Businesses would suffer, homes, schools and virtually every building would be submerged in water for days, and a number of young and the aged would die. The council of Ministers met with the King and devised a plan to prevent any further deaths. A majestic forty-story ship was built, and the citizens were advised to come aboard at the first sign of rainfall. Numerous hoardings were placed at various locations in the kingdom and a massive public-relations campaign was undertaken to make people aware about this 'Miraculous Life-saver', built at an exorbitant cost to save lives. The church and community leaders greatly applauded the efforts of the King and the ship was hailed as one of the biggest wonders of the universe.

The very first day that water poured down from the skies, everyone left their work midway and rushed to take shelter on the ship. Businesses, schools and other institutions had to close abruptly, and all activities came to a halt. While the rain came down heavily, it lasted for a mere two hours, and soon after the clouds slowly disappeared and the sun resurfaced. The citizens of the kingdom waited for a while, and when there was no sign of any further rain, they gradually descended to return to their respective jobs and chores. The day was, however, over and wasted, as no productive work could be accomplished by anyone.

The next time it rained, everyone was back on the ship again, but this time the downpour lasted for 15 days. Although the ship was built from the finest wood with the highest craftsmanship and safety standards, there was no suitable provision for sanitation. The emphasis had been on creating ample space to accommodate a larger number of people, while the crucial element of sanitation was completely ignored. From the third day onwards every floor was consumed with the foul smell of urine and feces that littered every corner. A number of young and old began falling sick, and with the first incident of Cholera, panic struck. As this disease spreads like wildfire when cleanliness and good sanitation are not available, the situation grew from bad to worse with each passing day. The number of people who were either vomiting or experiencing diarrhea kept increasing by the hour.

Before the rains eventually stopped and the citizens of the Kingdom could descend from the ship, seventy percent had perished, and the remaining were in a critical condition. Even members of the Royal family who had the privilege to be in the comfort of their executive suites were not spared, as disease does not favor the rich and everyone gets affected equally. A good number of the top elite including the Ministers and the Clergy also perished. The 'Miraculous Life-saver' had turned into a 'Tunnel of Death', from which only a few escaped alive.

The King and his council of Ministers could have thought of some other ways to counter the effects of Nature and save people from dying due to floods. Many natural alternatives, like underground drainage, to direct the rain-waters into rivers or lakes could have been implemented at a fraction of the cost. Even the excessive water that caused flooding and deaths could have been used productively to generate electricity or for agriculture. But due to the short-sightedness of those in power responsible to protect lives, an enormous amount of money was wasted on the so called life-saver, which rather turned into a life-destroyer.

The story of our 'Modern Medical Establishment' is very similar to this. They have spent trillions of dollars into research and development to produce the modern drugs to save people from dying due to sickness and disease. Over the years these drugs have been advertised as 'Miraculous Life-savers', just like that majestic ship the King got built at an exorbitant cost, which actually destroyed more lives than saved. The same holds true with these drugs and medications, which are not life-savers, but rather life-destroyers. When you begin to take them they do address the symptoms, just like the ship would have prevented deaths due to flooding. But gradually these drugs begin to destroy your vital organs and the natural functions of the human body. A casual dose of antibiotics for common colds will eventually lead to many other long-term complications. A drug to reduce high blood pressure can lead to diabetes, heart disease, kidney failure, and cancer. Neither of these so called miraculous drugs will actually heal any of the ailments; they will only add on to the existing toxic waste in your body and create more disease and death.

The majestic ship was not the answer to flooding, as it resulted into needless deaths and a sheer waste of money. The most economical and natural alternative could have been underground drainage, that would have not only prevented deaths due to flooding, but also directed the rain water into productive use. The same holds true for these modern drugs, as they are not the answer to cure any disease. Instead of wasting billions on their research and development, a natural alternative to drain the body from toxins and disease-causing bacteria could have easily been found and implemented.

Has any problem been resolved without finding the real cause? Once you find the reason, the next obvious step is practical implementation to eliminate the problem. No external doctor has the power to heal you, as that power lies with our internal doctor. Knowledge can indeed become extremely powerful when practically applied, and the greatest knowledge that exists in the universe is within us. To know who you really are and how the human body functions internally, is the most important part of that great knowledge.

It is truly amazing to realize that we are not human beings in search of a spiritual experience, rather spiritual beings having a human experience. This body is the home we reside in during our journey on earth, and the methods to keep it clean are no different than maintaining the physical home we live in. Regular daily inner cleansing with water is essential to drain out the toxins that lead to sickness and disease. My previous book, 'Mental, Physical and Spiritual Health', highlights the importance and benefits of drinking one and a half to two liters of water daily. If you do not have access to this book, you can visit my website, www. Humanityandlove.com, and check out the article 'Amazing Water Therapy', to know how water plays an instrumental role in keeping the inner body clean, and all organs in optimum health and vitality.

The most vital link to success in any area of our life is to make practical applications of the knowledge that comes our way, as that is the only way to ascertain its authenticity and determine if it works or not. For example, once you know that drinking one and a half to two liters of water daily can prevent and heal various health issues, only practical application will provide the required proof. But the most common problem with the human race is that a great number of people procrastinate, and don't even make an effort to try something new, unless they end up in a do-or-die situation. We need to change the way we live, and to avoid health problems the focus should be on prevention rather than rehabilitation.

In his wonderful book, "20,000 Days... and Counting", Robert D. Smith, describes this problem beautifully in these words: "There are tens of thousands of self-help books on the market, thousands of hours of audio and video recordings to impart life wisdom, nonstop "how-to-live" YouTube videos, and entire TV networks devoted to inspiration. Never before in human history have so many people been ready to discover their purpose in life. But you don't need a complicated system to get you on your way. The best preparation for living well is to be prepared to die at any time."

This is true – only if you can learn how to die, will you learn how to live – by making radical changes to your life. Steve Jobs in his Stanford Commencement speech said, "Remembering that you are going to die is the most important tool I've ever encountered to help me make the big choices in life. Because almost everything – all external expectations, all pride, all fear of embarrassment or failure – these things just fall away in the face of death, leaving only what is truly important. Remembering that you are going to die is the best way I know to avoid the trap of thinking you have something to lose. You are already naked. There is no reason not to follow your heart. Your heart knows what's right for you, don't be trapped by dogma – which is living with the results of other people's thinking. Listen to your heart, it somehow already knows what you truly want in life."

As a matter of fact, there's no need for you to actually die – you only have to allow all those habits to die that are a hindrance to your progress. Procrastination is one such habit that holds most people back from implementing knowledge that comes their way. Perhaps, you're not aware that the genes for supernatural success, health, and vitality have been permanently encoded into your spirit. If procrastination is holding you back from laying hands on what you so richly deserve, you've to allow it to die a natural death. Even in your body the cells are constantly dying and making room for new ones. Death, in the real sense of the word and even metaphorical sense, is very likely the single best invention of life. It is life's change agent, as it clears the old for the new. If you observe closely, there's nothing stagnant in Nature either, old flowers die and the plant gives birth to new ones. It's absolutely simple to follow the same very rule to allow old habits that hold you back from moving forward to die, and make room for new ones. Change is the only constant and permanent essence of life, and the only way to move forward is to Change, or else you will be left behind.

Chapter 2

It's All About Change

The Universe we live in is constantly changing, and this is one of the most amazing truths of it all. See how far you have come since the days of childhood and the vast changes that are affecting the lives of people on earth with each passing year. It's only change that moves you forward to become a better and more successful person. After all, the law of change is one of the profoundest laws in existence, and no matter what your present circumstances are, there will be a change for better or worse with or without your input. Obviously, if you decide to take control of your life and make efforts to bring change, then you've taken the responsibility to generate the required kind of outcome. Otherwise too, change will definitely come, but it may not be what you desire and could possibly make your situation worse than before.

If you look at the history of mankind, there are numerous people who applied this law successfully to get the desired outcome. The most recent was Barack Obama whose promise to bring about a change made him the first African American President of United States – the most powerful and prestigious position in the world. Simply using the law of change as a campaign slogan, his journey from being a junior senator from Illinois to the White House is a great example of the tremendous power of this law. What was that slogan? Change – We can believe in, and after that were the three most important words connected to this law – Yes we can. As his campaign moved on with the slogan of change to higher and higher grounds, this became no less than a national anthem. Rally after rally Senator Obama only had to utter these words, "Fellow Americans, we need to bring change we can believe in," and there used to be a loud and thunderous applause from his audience who in turn responded with – "Yes we can."

If Senator Barack Obama could use the law of change successfully to become President Obama, what can stop you from attaining your goals? It's nothing supernatural that he did, and there's nothing of that sort you have to do either. Simply understand how this law works, and make practical application of that knowledge in your daily activities. If procrastination is holding you back from attaining your goals, there is no need for any major concern. You should be happy to know you're not alone, as eighty percent of the world's population has the same habit.

If you need proof this is a valid percentage, simply look around at your family members and folks at work-place. Observe them carefully for a week, and you'll know how often they procrastinate and don't take any action on important issues affecting their work, lives, and health. This is just a minor but critical exercise to affirm how pandemic procrastination is. It is important that you analyze yourself meticulously to find out how deeply this habit is ingrained in you, how it has affected your life so far, and whether you want to move from the eighty to the twenty percent category. After that the most important question you need to ask yourself is this: Do I really want to make an effort to use the law of change and get procrastination out of my life? If you have answered yes, then you've made one of the greatest transformative decisions of your life. A decision to change and take control to become the captain of your ship and the master of your destiny.

Do you know the basic difference between the eighty and twenty percent categories? Many years ago, an enlightened man described it with these simple words: "Life is like a railroad, and the greater majority of people are like passenger coaches and freight cars. They do perform a useful service but cannot move on their own and have to be pushed or pulled by someone else. Only a few happen to be like the locomotives that not only move themselves but motivate countless others. Without them there would be no progress in the world, humanity would stagnate and eventually drift into savagery."

The eighty percent category consists of people who are like the passenger coaches and freight cars, while the twenty percent are like the locomotives. All the progress and inventions that have and are taking place to steer us forward and make our lives more comfortable, it is the twenty percent who are directly responsible for that. While the eighty percent are either enjoying the privileges derived from their hard work, or are struggling to understand the reasons behind their inability to move up in life, and thus fulfil their dreams and goals.

If you are in the eighty percent slot, you can easily move into the elite twenty percent club. The only hurdle in-between the two, is your habit of procrastination. It may surprise you to know that it's extremely easy to get rid of it by following a simple technique I have used since I was twenty years old. It is so simple that you may initially doubt whether it is authentic, and perhaps question if it would really work or not. But believe me, this has been one of the greatest tools responsible for the tremendous overall success I have attained in every area of my life.

Way back in December 1976 while searching for my first job, I met a fellow who shared a very powerful secret with me. I was in his office one afternoon when he showed me a piece of paper lying on his desk, which was basically his 'To Do List'. It was a plain paper on which he had noted several tasks, and they were numbered 1, 2, 3, and so on. He explained that he would keep adding any new assignments that came during the day, while taking action on the current ones. He would tick mark when a task was completed and prepare a new list in the evening for the following day, and never leave anything at the mercy of his memory. He further added: "I treat this list as very special, and things that most people will leave for tomorrow, I'll do them today, and what they would do today, I'll tackle them right now." Little did I realize at that time, this fellow was sharing a timeless secret of the universe on how to achieve great success in life.

A few days later I was hired, and from the very first day I began working with a 'To Do List'. Every single task that came my way would immediately go on to this list. I would tick mark when an assignment was completed, and every evening prepare a new list for the following day. I also began treating it as very special, and would do things today what most people will leave for tomorrow, and the tasks of today, I would handle them right away. This simple technique of having a list to work with began doing wonders in my professional and personal life, which even amazed me at that time. My Boss, colleagues, clients and suppliers had only good words about my work, and they all thought I possessed a supernatural memory. They were astonished at how even the smallest task never escaped my mind, and the way every single issue concerning their business or problems was taken care of promptly.

My immediate head in the company was the Business Manager, who was a qualified Chartered Accountant with many years of work experience behind him, and the Owner had high regard for his capabilities in steering the company forward. Due to some personal reasons he resigned two months after I joined, and all his work fell upon my shoulders. My designation, now as a Business Manager required me to handle the major operations of the company and here I was a young in-experienced twenty year old with no knowledge of my profile or qualifications to back me through. The only thing I did have, which turned out to be my greatest asset, was the 'To Do List', and a firm resolve to tackle every single assignment in the quickest and most efficient manner.

From the day he resigned and left, I began adding all tasks from his workload onto my list. Not even for a single day did I feel any undue pressure of the extra work or responsibilities, and none of the jobs he handled were neglected or not taken care of in a professional and timely manner. Initially, my Boss was planning to hire a new Business Manager with comparable qualifications and work experience, but after having seen my way of handling work for a couple of weeks, he rather promoted me officially to the position of a Business Manager. The 'To Do List' was working wonders for me, but it was not the list alone that was placing my career on a solid foundation.

There was another gem of an advice my cousin gave me the day I was leaving home to begin work. It was the first day of my first job, and I fondly remember when he took me aside and said: "Today you'll begin your work career and a new life of taking personal responsibility for your welfare, so let me tell you something important that may really help you in the long run. If you work like an employee, you will stay an employee your entire life. But if you work as you own this company, one day you'll have your own business entity. The choice is definitely yours in which way you wish to work, but the results will be in accordance with the decision you make today."

I clearly sensed the great mystical wisdom of the law of

sow and reap hidden in these simple, yet profound words. If I worked like an employee, I would obviously sow such seeds of employment and reap accordingly, by remaining an employee all my life. On the other hand, if I worked as if I was the owner of this company, those seeds of personal responsibility and expansion will lead me to having my own business one day. Following this life-changing and enlightening advice from my cousin, and equipped with the magical powers of a 'To Do List', today I stand tall with a sense of fulfilment for how far I've come and attained supernatural success in every segment of my life.

A few years back I attended Yanik Silver's Underground Internet Marketing Training in Los Angeles. There were many well-known business millionaires who were guest speakers at this amazing event, and they shared some of their success stories and secrets. A good number of them attributed their overall success mainly to a 'To Do List', and one very successful entrepreneur explained in detail how he carried a mini-recorder with him at all times. Any time a task or idea came to his mind he would record it immediately, and then later take action on it. He even suggested to the audience that they should buy and carry their mini-recorders to the bathroom as well, as this is what he does, because a number of creative thoughts usually come in the mornings, and one should never miss to record them.

It's all about Change, and that's what you need to move forward in life. The widespread habit of procrastination may be the only element holding you back from all the success and happiness that is an eternal part of your genetic coding. So the first step in Going Back to Nature and healing yourself is to change this habit. Instead of being a procrastinator – you need to become an Action-taker. If Senator Obama could successfully utilize the Law of Change to become President Obama, there is virtually no reason why you cannot do the same and become what you want to be. The 'To Do List' is what you need to begin with to change the habit of procrastination. Once there is a list of work-to-do in front of you and a resolve to do today what most people will leave for tomorrow, and do now, what most will leave for later, you will get on the road of becoming an action-taker, and not a procrastinator.

The second thing you need to change is your 'attitude' towards work. If you work for someone, change your basic way of thinking and start working as if you own the company. Stop expecting what your boss or the company should do for you, rather move your thought process in the opposite direction, and see what you can do for them. How can sales be increased, services improved, and expenses reduced. This is one of the little unknown secrets behind the success of many people who have greatly progressed in life. It's a mindset you need to develop to get attuned to the universal law of sow and reap. Once you give your company the seeds of hard work and dedication without any conditions attached, there's no way – you will not be noticed. The rewards will arrive in multiple ways through promotions, bonuses, and bigger responsibilities. In fact, the sky is the limit for the fellow who works in such a manner.

If you are a business owner, think about your products or services as if they are for your own use, and then set bench marks for quality, performance, and price as you would expect to receive from others. Every business needs profits, but an enormous amount is not required at any given time. Rather, it is a steady flow that takes a business higher and higher. Do you need a lot of food at one time to survive, or a regular daily supply? Any product or service that is high on value but low on price is bound to succeed in the long run. After all, it's not short-term profits that matter, but rather how you end up on the success ladder in the long run is the most pivotal factor in life. Your work, products, or services should always reflect the long run attitude.

A perfect example of the long run attitude is the rock group known as 'The Eagles', and they even have a song and album titled 'The Long Run'. Over the last few years I have had the privilege to attend four of their concerts, including the latest - 'History of the Eagles'. Mostly at every concert, they talk about how they broke up as a group in 1980 and reunited in 1994, and then they usually perform the song 'The Long Run', which has words like: 'I used to hurry a lot, I used to worry a lot, did you do it for love, did you do it for money, we can handle some resistance if our love is a strong one, who is going to make it, we'll find out in the long run.' They claim this song and words truly describe the reasons that led to their breakup, reunion, unity, and the success that has come their way.

Incidentally, The Long Run was their last studio album before they broke up in 1980. As each of them went their separate way into solo careers, none found the kind of success they had attained as 'The Eagles'. I believe, the words of this song must have kept haunting them, as each member could very well relate to these meaningful lyrics – I used to hurry a lot, I used to worry a lot. Perhaps, the hurry and worry was one reason for all the stress that came and led to their breakup. Maybe, they kept asking themselves – Did I do it for love, or did I do it for money? The words – We can handle some resistance if our love is a strong one, and who is going to make it, we'll find out in the long run, must have definitely paved the way for the reunion of the group in 1994.

When they got back together for an MTV presentation, one of the members, Glen Frey, remarked – that they never really broke up, but took a fourteen year vacation. Such was the power and impact of the long run attitude. Since then, The Eagles have not looked back, and with each passing year have been soaring higher and higher, just like an eagle does. They have been touring extensively around the world and became the first rock group to perform in China. In July 2013, they began a new tour called History of the Eagles and have been repeatedly performing in major cities in the USA, Canada, Ireland, United Kingdom, Europe, New Zealand and Australia to packed houses. When they announced three shows in January 2014 at the newly renovated Forum in Los Angeles, they got sold out in a couple of days forcing them to add three more shows in the same month.

If the long run attitude helped The Eagles to change and reunite to become the greatest rock band in history books, there's no reason why it cannot help you to become the greatest person you can possibly be. If you can get rid of your hurry and worry, if you start doing whatever you do with love, if you can handle some resistance and change your habit of procrastination – you will certainly make it in the long run.

Chapter 3

Knowing your 'Self'

The long run attitude is the reality of our existence in this amazing universe that we are a part and parcel of, a universe that has, and is continually expanding since the beginning of creation. Or we can even say, the universe has been moving forward and expanding with the long run attitude, which means, there is no end to it.

The reality of the expanding universe was first stated in the Indian Vedas that are over 5000 years old and considered to be one of the oldest existing scriptures of knowledge. The sages of that era made this discovery due to their enlightened state of being. They also analyzed the working of the human body, examining how the cells and organs were in a constant state of change and creation, and drew parallels with the universe. They considered the human body to be a mini-universe containing everything that the actual universe had. Today, many scientists have reaffirmed through their scientific research the same truth of the ever expanding universe. They have found evidence that it is in a constant state of change and creation and has been expanding since its inception.

In fact, there are three possible theories of expansion that exist, and each of them predict a different fate for the universe in the long run. The three types of expanding universe are called – open, flat, and closed. If the universe was open, then it would expand forever. If it was flat, it would also expand, but the expansion would slow down to zero after a certain amount of time. In the third scenario, if the universe was closed, it would stop expanding and eventually re-collapse on itself.

The theory of the three types of universe is analogous to us human beings. If our mind is open and we are ready to learn from every single event or opportunity that comes our way, then we would expand much like the universe and progress forever. If our mind is flat, that is, we take little or no action to learn from those events or opportunities, then we would still expand, but the expansion would slow down to zero after a certain amount of time. Lastly, if our mind is closed, and we are not ready to accept or learn anything from the unfolding scenarios, then the expansion would stop and eventually re-collapse on itself. In other words, we will stay as we are without any improvement in any segment of our lives.

Knowing your Self is to know who you are in reality. Some people consider or believe they are basically the human body itself – one day they'll die and that would be the end of their existence. These are the Type 3 with closed minds, not ready to accept or learn anything from whatever happens in their life. They don't make any effort to explore the mysteries surrounding their existence on earth, nor realize the wondrous nature of the universe. So when they eventually die, it is a situation of re-collapsing and remaining in the same form as they originally came in.

Then, we have a second group of people who feel there is an unseen element attached to the human body, a soul or spirit, and upon physical death they may go to a place called heaven or hell based upon their deeds, but they're not certain about it. These are the Type 2 with flat minds, who take little or no action to find out the truth about themselves or learn from the unfolding events or endeavor to discover the mysteries of life. Accordingly, their expansion slows down to zero after a certain amount of time, and they spend their lives on earth filled with doubts and fears of every kind. They hardly achieve any major success, and often feel that people or some unknown forces are responsible for their misfortunes and misery. This group greatly depends on prayer and asking for favors from God all the time.

Type 1 with open minds are extremely rare to find, but it's through them that the world has progressed so far. These are the folks responsible for the wonderful inventions and great discoveries that has led to all the progress since the Stone Age. Keeping an open mind and a willingness to learn from their mistakes is the key to their ever-expanding knowledge and success. This group understands the importance of 'Knowing your Self', and once they realize who they are and discover their inner powers, they use them fearlessly for their own advancement and also of their fellow beings.

Knowing your Self is one of the greatest teachings contained in every scripture of every religion, but it's only people with open minds who are able to understand and make practical application to get acquainted with their true Self. To keep an open mind is the key to the ultimate discovery of who you are and the powers of creation that are an integral part of you.

A great number of years ago, the seven sages of ancient Greece who laid the foundation for western culture, gathered in Delphi to inscribe the sacred words – 'Know Thyself' at the entry to their Temple. These words opened the way for many people to seek their true identity and discover the reality of their existence in the universe. Before the Greeks, the Hindus in India had developed their own philosophy on knowledge of the Self. In one of their ancient scriptures known as 'Upanishads', it is clearly outlined – "Enquiry into the truth of the Self is real knowledge." Over the years countless authors, poets, and philosophers have repeatedly written and spoken about the importance of this inner journey. In every religion, culture, ethnicity, and age, this has been talked about by several sages and eminent personalities.

Around 400 BC, Plato, the great Greek philosopher and mathematician expressed this knowing and the issues related to it in these beautiful words: "The soul is a helpless prisoner, chained hand and foot in the body, compelled to view reality not directly, but only through its prison bars, and wallowing in utter ignorance. Philosophy takes over the soul in this condition and encourages it to collect and concentrate itself by itself, trusting nothing but its own independent judgment. Philosophy is, therefore, the art and science of dissecting soul from body. It is a task available to all yet pursued by few."

To explain the meaning of 'Know Thyself', the Upanishads portray a story of a young boy being taught the mystical mysteries of the Self. This boy having witnessed his father's traditional observance of Hindu customs, inquires whether it is possible to survive death, and if so, by which means. He is told in a profound dialogue that ensued, "The Self lies beyond the senses and can only be understood by him who knows it, and those who realize the Self are forever free from the jaws of death. This doubt haunted even the Gods of old, for the secret of death is hard to know. Those hypnotized by the world of sense, 'I am my body; when my body dies, I die' fall life after life, and the key to surviving death is transferring one's identity from the bodily senses to the Self, and those who will know the Self will become the Self. This should be Man's ultimate goal in life."

In the 20th century, George Gurdjieff, an influential spiritual teacher in Europe, outlined that there were different states of consciousness for man, and under normal conditions man was more like a sleeping machine. In this state of self-ignorance he was enslaved to his indulgences, fears and insecurities, which have full control over him, because he does not know himself. The first and foremost reason for man's inner slavery was his ignorance of himself. Without self-knowledge, man cannot be free, he cannot take charge of himself and will always remain a slave. That is why in all ancient teachings, 'Know Thyself' is the first step at the conception of the path to liberation. He clearly emphasized that Awakening was possible only for those who seek it and want it, and are ready to struggle and work on themselves persistently in order to attain it. Only one must know how to learn, as knowledge can only be acquired by a suitable and complete study, no matter what the starting point is. To know thyself, you must begin with the study of your Self.

Have you ever thought, why does the vast disparity between the rich and poor, successful and unsuccessful, healthy and unhealthy, keeps growing? Why only a handful of people and a small percentage of businesses are really successful in the long run? The reason is quite obvious. It's only a handful who take the plunge to detach the soul from the body and get acquainted with their true Self – the innermost core that houses the greatest treasure and creative powers of the universe. This is a task available to all, to discover and unleash our true potential, but pursued only by a few, as the majority believe that it is futile to waste time on such a useless expedition of knowing your Self. They feel, what's there to know after all? One day death will arrive, so why not make hay while the sun still shines.

A great many years ago, there lived a beggar named Smiley in a small town in the south of India. He was a sweet natured man, slightly physically challenged from birth, and always had a smile on his face. Most of the town dwellers knew him well as he sat next to a famous holy temple from early morning to late evening. He knew the majority of them by their first names and always had some words of cheer and inspiration to share whenever they stopped by to give him alms. He had a unique way of conversing and blessing people, accompanied with an amazing heart-warming smile.

Finally, a day came when his time on earth was up. As he lay there taking his last few breaths on the spot where he had spent over 50 years of his life, he disclosed his heart's desire. It was his wish that he should be buried right there. Arrangements were made for burial the following day in accordance to his wish. As a number of townsmen gathered to give Smiley a final farewell, two laborers began digging the ground. Having dug about six feet, their tools hit a metal obstruction, which made them dig deeper and wider. Eventually, they came across a huge golden container. The crowd was simply awe-struck and amazed with what they saw, and curiosity took the better part of them as to what may be inside.

The Head-priest of the temple was invited to come open it, and as he lifted the lid, there lay a grand treasure of gold and ruby ornaments worth millions. People stood there spellbound and mesmerized, their eyes filled with surprise and disbelief. No one could believe that a grand treasure worth millions was right under the place where the poor beggar had sat all his life, begging for alms to have his daily bread. If he knew what was below him, all he had to do was to dig about ten feet and get hold of this wealth, and then live like a King for the rest of his life. The question is, had he known? If he did, would he have made the effort to dig or live at the mercy of alms donated by people to ensure his survival?

This story is of course a fable, but it points toward the hidden treasure lying within each of us. A treasure that cannot be measured by any amount of wealth, as it's priceless. If you can dig within and get hold of it, you too can live like a King for the rest of your life. This is what 'Know Thyself' is all about – to find out who you are and the powers contained in your Spirit. Since millennia, people of un-questionable authority, be it, spiritual, philosophers, authors, inventors or successful businessmen, have all shared one common belief – to know your Self is the greatest and most important expedition in life. Scriptures of every world religion also confirm the same reality. So then, why does the majority of mankind not understand this simple truth? A truth that would lead to a new world, a new order, where everyone would find success and there would be no poverty, homeless people, or needless wars and terrorism.

It is highlighted in several scriptures and modern books of knowledge that if we look carefully and observe Nature, we can find the truth about our real personality. To make such an observation, we need to look no further than into the life of a tiny little spider. There are two important elements that we shall focus upon, and the first one deals with how a spider builds a web to live and catch his prey – a web that is so artistic yet technical.

To make a web the spider releases silk from its spinnerets

and jumps from one end to the other, leaving a long horizontal thread connecting both sides. Then, it jumps to a third end releasing silk in the process, and eventually goes back to the original starting point. This process produces two radials which are connected to make a strong Y-shaped center. More radials are added, while ensuring that the distance between each is small enough to cross. The spider will use its own body for measurements, and after the radials are complete, fortify the center of the web with five or six circular threads. The spaces between each radial are directly proportional to the distance from the tip of the spider's back legs to its spinners. After the web is complete, it chews off the initial three center threads to make room to sit and wait for the prey.

It is quite possible you may have never looked at a spider's web to know how artistically it is made and the unique technical aspects behind it. Have a good look at the photograph on the adjoining page and try to determine what kind of superior intelligence a minute creature is equipped with to build such a masterpiece. If a spider has such an amazing intelligence, what about you? It is said, Man was created as the most supreme being who by the virtue of his intelligence would control the planet and his dominance would prevail on all the other species. Perhaps, you've never viewed yourself in that light, never thought about the supernatural intelligence you are equipped with or the wondrous hidden powers of creation that are an integral part of your being. To 'Know Thyself' in simple terms is to know who you are, the powers you possess and your unlimited capabilities.

A Spider's Web

The second important element of a spider's nature is that it never gives up in the face of adversity. During construction, if the wind destroys the web or brings the spider down, it immediately rises and starts building again. There is a popular ancient tale that was a part of my junior school studies, and it highlights this unique aspect of a spider's character. Once upon a time, there was a king named Arjuna whose kingdom was taken away by an invading army of the Moguls, headed by a ruthless leader. As he was defeated and had to run for his life, he took shelter in a cave. While he lay there in hopelessness and despair, an amazing scene captured his attention. A spider was trying to weave a web across the cave ceiling, and fell down. Almost immediately it was up, and climbed back to continue with the work. A short while later a strong surge of wind came and destroyed part of the web, and the spider was down again. Slowly, it got up once again and began re-building. It was almost done, when another surge destroyed the web in the same manner.

The little spider was unaffected by all these hurdles and destruction, and every time got back to rebuilding with the same force and courage, as if nothing had happened. Finally, after jumping around from one end to the other and falling several times, the web was successfully completed. A strong surge of wind came once again, but the web had been reinforced to handle such shocks to avoid any further damage. Rather, this time the web moved like a swing with the force of the wind, and the spider was seated in the center of the web on the throne it had made for itself, and was enjoying the thrilling ride.

Having witnessed this life inspiring act of courage and persistence, Arjuna said to himself, "If a little spider can face failure so bravely and re-build its web with the same energy and strength, how can I give up so easily and feel depressed about what happened? I too will not relent and use all my powers and intelligence to prepare and attack the invaders to regain my lost kingdom." The spider's determination in face of great adversity gave tremendous courage to the defeated king, as he got out of the cave to begin the task of regaining his throne. He got hold of his soldiers who were wandering in the woods aimlessly with a low morale, and told them the amazing story of the spider. He thought of new ways of fighting against a large army and trained his men to have faith, courage, and develop a 'never give-up' attitude. On their first attempt, his army was again defeated by the Moguls, but that did not deter his spirit. Instead, he sat down to analyze what he was doing wrong and invented new methods to train his men in guerilla warfare. Eventually, after multiple incursions into the enemy strongholds, he finally regained his kingdom.

So what are the two major traits a spider has? A unique intelligence to build a complex web without any outside help, and a never give up attitude. Compare these to the reality of who you are – the ultimate of all creations on planet Earth, superior to all other species in every form. The spider can only build the same web, and this is what it has been doing since time immemorial with great finesse and persistence. In other words, the spider is an expert in the work it does, a real craftsman of the highest caliber, and its dedication to the task at hand is unparalleled and matched by an unflinching persistent and courageous nature.

When you begin to know your Self, one of the most important realizations that will dawn upon you is, that you are equipped with an inborn talent to become a master craftsman in a certain field. The only thing that you need to do is find out what that talent is, and then practice, practice, and practice till you become an expert. Mahatma Gandhi who realized this unique human potential, said: "Man often becomes what he believes himself to be. If I keep on saying to myself that I cannot do a certain thing, it is possible that I may end up becoming incapable of doing it. On the contrary, if I shall have the belief that I can do it, I shall surely acquire the capacity to do it, even if I may not have had it at the beginning."

In case you do not believe it is important to 'Know your Self' or you question what is there after all to know, then you will become what you believe in. If you believe that you are merely an ordinary human being, then everything you'll do will be ordinary, and you will ultimately end up of being incapable of doing anything beyond ordinary. This kind of mind frame will lead you to live an ordinary existence with ordinary success, and you will often wonder, how others accomplish extraordinary things and achieve extraordinary success. Life will remain as an unresolved mystery for you.

The truth is, you have the potential to resolve the mystery of your existence on Earth right now. All you need to do is take a journey within to get acquainted with who you truly are. If you'll begin with the belief 'I can do it', then you will surely acquire the capacity, even if you may not have had it at the beginning. Nothing is difficult, it's all a perception of your mind which can make things possible or impossible. Knowing your Self is not a difficult thing at all, but you have to believe in the importance of this vital and life-changing journey. As you are the Master of your Destiny, it is your choice that eventually matters – you can either live like Smiley, the beggar who sat on a container of gold and begged for alms all his life, or you can learn from a spider, as to how it does its work with such great precision and a never give up attitude.

Have you ever looked at a bumblebee which defies the basic law of nature by flying? According to scientists, the bumblebee's body is too heavy and the wing span too small, and aerodynamically it's impossible for it to fly. But the bumblebee does not know this fact and keeps flying and continuing with its life's work. If you realized you had no limitations, then what would you do? As a matter of fact, the only limitations we have are those which are self-imposed, and the simple reason is that we do not know our true potentialities. We are born with supernatural powers and an infinite amount of untapped talent. We just need to believe in our potential and give a channel to the reservoir of energy and talent that we possess.

As we now move on to the next chapter in our journey of Going Back to Nature, the importance of beginning your personal journey into knowing your Self cannot be under-scored. In fact, as you will soon find out, there's no greater journey, no greater joy, and no greater work than to un-leash your true and unlimited possibilities. The only obstacle that stands between you and the real you, is your Mind. It is the mind that holds you back from discovering who you are. One of my previous books, "The Conscious, Unconscious and Super-Conscious Mind", explains in detail how the mind functions, and the art of balancing its three segments to get acquainted with your true identity. You should consider this as a course book on life, as it can greatly help you in the journey of knowing your Self.

Chapter 4

The Truth will set you Free

S ince time immemorial, Teachers of great wisdom have repeated this reality again and again – The truth will set you free. The universe we live in works in a very orderly fashion and nothing happens by chance – this is one major universal truth. As we all are an integral part of the universe, the same truth also applies to us. Everything that relates to our lives on earth moves in a very orderly fashion, and nothing happens by chance or mere coincidence. It doesn't matter whether we actively participate knowingly in the creation process, as creation is happening through us even un-knowingly. This is one of the most important realizations you can ever have – that you truly are the creator of your destiny and responsible for all the events that unfold in your life.

According to ancient wisdom, out of all the places in this ever-expanding universe, Earth is regarded as a critical learning center, where the truth of your real personality will be gradually unveiled through proper education. The word education is derived from the Latin word educare, which means to bring out what is inside you, or to lead you from ignorance to knowledge or from darkness to light. Education in essence means to unravel who you truly are, to get acquainted with your Soul and inborn talent to become an expert in a field that perfectly fits your personality. But the current system of education does the complete opposite. Instead of bringing out, they keep on pouring into you the subjects that teach you how to earn in a comfortable manner, how to survive in a cutthroat business environment, and how to rise up on the corporate ladder. They try to provide you all the tools to help you succeed in the outer world, but fail to provide a single tool to help you connect to your inner world and bring out the hidden treasures lying within you.

A tiger is born as a tiger and will stay and die as a tiger, doing the same activities again and again. There is no hidden potential that he can explore to do anything else, and the same holds true for all other animals. It's only us, humankind, who are actually born as a seed in the human body, a seed with unlimited potential. Just like there are different seeds for each plant, we too are seeds of different kinds. That is why no two people are alike, be it in the way they think, speak, act, or look. We all are individuals having a unique personality with an ever-expanding potential to grow and complete our evolution on earth. In fact, we are missionaries with a mission to become the best that we can, and serve or entertain others with our talents, products or services.

To give you an example of how true education works, let's have a brief look at the lives of three tennis legends – Rafael

Nadal, Novak Djokovic, and Serena Williams. They all began playing tennis at the early ages of three and four, when their inner talent was discovered by their family members. True education was provided to bring out what was inside of them to help the seed reach its ultimate potential. It's not as if they were born as champions, but the unlimited potential was there, which was harnessed with the right education and training to turn them into what they were meant to be. Rafael Nadal has created history by winning nine French Open championships and 14 Grand Slams overall. Novak Djokovic has been the world number one for a record 182 weeks and has won 11 Grand Slams, while Serena Williams has 21 Grand Slams to her credit and has been the world number one for 260 weeks overall. It's a marvel to watch them play such great tennis and make unbelievable shots of the highest caliber. At times it seems as if angels have descended from the skies, in their forms, to entertain and inspire us with immaculate stroke play.

These three extraordinary people are just examples I have picked to illustrate the meaning of true education, but there are numerous others in various professions who were guided into the right field at a young age, in line with their inborn talents. The success these people have attained is an authentic proof of the importance of the right kind of education, that is, not to pour into you what you do not need, but to bring out what you already have, and to help develop your seed of unlimited potential to the fullest.

The truth will indeed set you free. Imagine, if Rafael

Nadal, Novak Djokovic, and Serena Williams had gone through the regular standardized education system, and turned into engineers or doctors, instead of tennis players? Would the world not have been deprived of their unique talent? Additionally, there is every possibility they would not have succeeded in any other profession. Why should it be left to the family to discover the unique talent of their children, when this should be an integral part of our education system? A great majority of people are an absolute misfit in the work they're currently doing. Although, they may have acquired the requisite degree for that trade, it does not match their inborn talent. This results in their inability to excel and real success eludes them, leading to frustration, stress, and low productivity.

Albert & Comfort Ocran in their book, 'The Five-Talent Mentality' highlight the reality behind our unique individual talents and abilities with this wonderful story: Many years ago, there was a man who played the piano in a bar. He was very good at what he did and many people came out daily just to hear him play. However, one night a patron told him he didn't want to hear him just play anymore. He wanted him to also sing a song. "I don't sing!" the pianist protested. But the customer was persistent. He told the bartender, "I'm tired of listening to the piano. I want that guy to sing!" The pianist who had never sung in public, did so for the very first time. And nobody had ever heard the song Mona Lisa sung the way it was rendered that night by Nat King Cole, and he eventually became a music legend and a household name. He always had the talent but he was sitting on it. He may have lived the rest of his life as an anonymous pianist playing daily in an insignificant bar, but because he was "forced" to sing, he went on to become one of the best-known entertainers in America.

In the olden times the system of education was very different. Teachers were closely involved with the students as compared to now, and the focus was more on finding their in-born talents and training them appropriately. The goal was not to make them a part of the rut to do the conventional, but to bring out their inherent talent and then hone it with the right kind of education and training. In India before the British arrived, this kind of education system was in place. The schools, known as Gurukuls, offered free education and no external authorities or politics were permitted to enter or control the school system. Access to good education was not dependent on wealth, but rather on talent. If this kind of education existed today, there would not be such a gross imbalance between the rich and poor or the successful and unsuccessful.

The education system we all have gone through is the number one reason for the majority of our misfortunes, failures, and related stress. It's all about change, and if you agree that the style and concept of education needs to be changed to benefit the future generations, there is something each of us needs to do. We should never leave such matters that affect us and the future of our children entirely in the hands of the government and educational authorities. The attitude should not be 'what can they do for us', rather, it should investigate what we can do for ourselves. A community that has joined hands for any project or initiative has always found success in the long run. There's so much you can do by getting involved with the school and local authorities to bring change into our education system.

I have personally taken the initiative to build such schools in Ghana from the proceeds earned from the sales of my books. The first school is now under construction in Accra, and should be ready to commence operations in 2018. Besides providing the best available education, the school will have a finer arts facilities to include classes in modern and traditional music, singing, painting, nutrition, health, drama, speech, and dancing. It will also be equipped with studios for visual and performing arts, and have facilities for tennis, basketball, hockey, soccer, and athletics. The primary goal will be to create a new generation of citizens of the universe in an environment that takes care of their holistic development from childhood, and evolve them into not just ordinary, but extraordinary adults.

Every child has a unique inborn talent, generosity, and love in his heart. True education means to help children discover these virtues in an atmosphere of joy and fun with activities that engage all of their five sense modalities. The focus will be to teach and create a conducive environment that fosters creative thought and action, and to hone their inherent talents to optimize their best potential. For example, if a child is good at singing, besides providing the best available education, the primary focus would be to whet the child's vocal skills to become a good singer. Likewise, if someone is good in sports, drama, accounting or business, they will be trained and educated to become professionals in those spheres. Imagine, if each of us were an expert in our professions, what could be the quality of services and products available to everyone?

Ken Robinson, in his eye-opening book, 'Creative Schools', highlights the problems faced by our schooling system and suggests adequate changes to make education work in the right manner. He gives an example of a formula that was applied in a school in Atlanta with the lowest academic performance in the district. The most remarkable application the principal and staff made was to make students feel valued, by dealing with each of them according to their needs and interests. They felt it was important to have a good curriculum, but the interest of each student was far more important than that. If football was what the student was passionate about, they weren't going to give precedence to math or science over the sport, as they wanted the education to be passion driven rather than following what conventional curriculum demands. When they began taking this approach and the students saw that the school valued what they valued, they started giving them back what they valued. Once they began building relationships by focusing on what the child wanted, and the same child may not have liked English or science, there was no way he would let his teachers down. So the students put an extra effort to do well at purely academic syllabi too as they realized that the school was focusing on making them excel at what they were truly passionate about, be it music, drama, sport and the likes.

This unique approach was completely different from the model of education coming from the state and federal authorities, but it began doing wonders for the school and students. There was a student who failed the sixth grade, but was a good athlete. The school agreed that athletics was the most important thing in his life. As they encouraged and helped him to become a better athlete, he began to pass every test. Another student whose father had died when she was in the fourth grade, could not pass the sixth grade. The chorus teacher saw a unique talent in her and gave her a solo song to prepare and perform. Once she did that, she showed drastic improvement in her studies, and got all A's for the rest of the year. The teacher said that you have to see what is important to the child, and all this girl wanted was to sing. When they gave her what she wanted, she began to give them what they wanted. Test scores of the school went up by sixty percent in every group, and the school was named the Georgia Title 1 Distinguished School and the 2011 MetLife Foundation-NASSP Breakthrough School. The principal, Laurie Barron, was named 2013's MetLife NASSP National Middle Level Principal of the year.

This is what the essence of education was in the ancient times, and this is where we need to return. Teachers have to closely work with their students, see what they want and observe them carefully to discover their unique talents and help them individually. As the path-breaking formula applied in this modern school in USA worked so profoundly, it becomes evident that when a child is helped in his interests, the grades in other subjects are also bound to improve. It's not as if a student who becomes a professional footballer, athlete or a singer, will not complete schooling with an overall development in other subjects important for his growth and evolvement. Rather, when the school helps the child to become what he wants to be, the performance in other subjects improves exponentially.

Ken explains that the current system of mass education came into being in the 19th century with the dawn of the industrial revolution, and the principles of manufacturing were applied to it. For example, in the manufacturing sector, similar types of items are produced in accordance with preset standards and specifications. The same formula was applied to education to make students compliant to certain standards. While producing goods the value of the relevant raw materials is generally overlooked, and the focus is rather on the products being produced. This is what happened with our education system. The focus is entirely on curriculum, teaching, and assessment, while the real talents and interests of students, which are the actual raw materials to work with, are overlooked. We should not forget that human beings are not products manufactured in factories and one formula cannot work evenly for everyone, as each individual is different and unique in nature and characteristics. This system of mass education does nothing to help students discover their talents and true capabilities, which ultimately leads to a sense of lack and frustration in their lives, work, and relationships. Frustration in the sense that most people spend their whole life living 'someone else's life', implying that they haven't ever followed their heart and found their true calling in life. The lives they live and the work they do is what the education system has prescribed to them.

The school authorities, governments, and regulatory agencies don't realize the damage being inflicted on students through this industrial standardized mass education system. We all have different strengths and weaknesses, different talents and capabilities. Personalization means teachers taking account of these differences in how they teach different students and tailoring their teaching methodology in cognizance with the student's unique disposition. It also means allowing for flexibility within the curriculum so that in addition to what all students need to learn in common, there are opportunities for them to pursue their individual interests and strengths as well.

You should read this wonderful book by Ken Robinson to realize the transformations that are required at the grassroots level and what each of us can do. I'll personally take a lot of ideas from his writings and possibly seek his help and guidance, when setting up the system of education in the up-coming school in Ghana. A school that will be known as 'Healthy Mind International – A school of the future, for the children of today'. This school will have classes beginning from Kindergarten to High School, and 25 percent of the seats will be reserved for children from under-privileged families who will have access to free education.

Due to this modern system of mass education, we have been gradually losing touch with our real self, but the time has now arrived for us to go back to the basics. There's nothing you can do about the way you were educated, but if you believe you are a child of God or a Creator, then who are you really? For example, a child of a dog is called a pup, but then, it's his destiny to grow up and become a dog one day. Not the same dog like his father or mother, but a dog in his own right, and nothing can stop that process of nature. Likewise, if you are a child of God or a Creator, it's also your destiny to grow up and become a God or a Creator one day. Not the same God or Creator you may be worshipping and holding in high esteem, but a God or Creator in your own right, and nothing can stop this due process of nature.

When you will get to know yourself better, this is one truth that will raise questions in your head again and again. The greatest of all creations on earth is Man and Woman, and don't they both collectively have the power to create life? Who is responsible for all the amazing creations, like electricity, cars, aero-planes, computers, internet, cell-phones etc.? The world has become so close-knit where you can talk and see each other on cell-phones and laptops, no matter how far the distance may be. Who has created all these heavenly gadgets? Are these not our very own creations, and does that not prove that we are creators with the power of creation running through our veins?

The truth that will eventually set you free from living an ordinary existence will be the realization that we are all Gods or Creators in the making. People who know this reality are the ones who keep on honing their inner talents to improve and become masters in their field. These are the folks responsible for bringing about change with their amazing inventions, discoveries and innovations. The child of a dog will physically turn into a dog from a pup after a certain time, but in our case, the situation is a little different. It's not as we grow physically that we shall automatically turn into a God or Creator. This is rather dependent not on physical, but spiritual growth.

The question you may ask is, how do we grow in spirit? The answer is simple. When we find our unique inborn talent and begin to work upon it through learning, practice, and repetition to become the best that we can possibly be, it's then that we grow in spirit. And when we begin to serve others fruitfully with that talent, we begin the work as a God or Creator on Earth. For example, by winning numerous Grand Slams, not only have Rafael Nadal, Novak Djokovic, and Serena Williams demonstrated their godly and creative talents to entertain millions of people, but they have also inspired them with an amazing display of unlimited human possibilities.

We have been on Earth since thousands of years, and why are we still here? The reason is quite obvious. Until we don't complete our education in this most important learning center of the universe, and graduate from Human-kind to

God or Creative-kind, and then perform the related work, we will continue to return again and again. To graduate, we need to discover our unique inborn talents and become experts or masters in line with our true capabilities, and eventually serve, entertain, or inspire others with our talents, products and services.

There is a beautiful story that depicts this reality about our journey on Earth. Once there was a King who had three sons: Paul, George, and Peter. He had closely observed them as they were growing up and was well acquainted with their individual inborn talents. It was his desire to help them attain the right kind of education and training to become masters in their field of expertise, and then serve the people of his kingdom with their talents. So one fine day he invited them to his chambers to hand them some very important assignments.

He told Paul to leave for England to become a master musician, and explained how essential it was to entertain and educate people of the Kingdom with music, to take away their worries and help them become more productive. George was directed to head to the USA and become a master in Information Technology. He told him how important it was to modernize the nation with computers and other related gadgets, to advance the lives of people and help them connect with the outside world. Peter was asked to leave for India to study natural medicine and the mysteries of life and death from the sages and spiritual masters, and to turn into a master healer to guide people of the Kingdom on to the path of good health and self-realization.

To each of his sons he gave a bag containing one million dollars, to cater for the related expenses of their individual missions. He explained in very gentle words, that they should return back to the kingdom only after the required mastery had been attained. Although the million dollars would more than suffice for the purpose, but in case more was required, they could briefly return and take another million, and more, if need be. There was no restriction on how much money would be required overall and no time frame to accomplish their missions. The only condition to return back to the kingdom permanently and serve the people with their talents, was to become masters in the assigned fields.

The three sons left for their respective destinations with the money in hand. Paul arrived in London to become a master musician, but in a matter of weeks got lost in the British way of life. Staying up late at night in the neighborhood pubs, getting intoxicated with a mixture of the world's most exotic drinks and love affairs with multiple girls became the norm. With so much money in hand, he didn't really know what to do and began to spend recklessly. Finally, one day the funds were depleted, and it was only then he remembered that his father had sent him to become a master musician. So there was no option other than to return home, and get a million more to complete the forgotten mission.

The second son, George, landed in New York with his father's instructions fresh in his mind to become a master in Information Technology. He was totally mesmerized by the American lifestyle, the freedom of expression and the beauty he saw around him. One night, a trip to Manhattan and 42nd Street changed his life completely, and he too started spending recklessly on women and highly intoxicating drugs. He began to deeply enjoy this unique way of life and got totally lost in the world of drugs and women. The mission his father had assigned was totally forgotten, until the day he found that the million dollars were almost gone. He was ashamed at what he had done, but the only available option was to return back and get one more million to complete the mission.

The third son, Peter, reached Haridwar, a city in India famous for the holy river Ganges, and where several spiritual healers and masters lived. He remembered his father's instructions very well, and considered the task at hand as an assignment from God. From day one the mission was clear as crystal in his mind and heart, to study under the renowned spiritual healers and masters, learn the art of natural healing, and discover the mysteries of life and death. He became a disciple of Gurudev, one of the greatest Hindu healer and spiritual master of that era. Under the tutelage of his Guru he had to live a simple, pious life in an Ashram, which was similar to a boarding school with strict discipline and a unique pure way of life.

It took two years for Peter to turn into a natural healer, and discover the secrets of the mind, body and spirit. He studied the Hindu scriptures with great zeal to learn about the mysteries of life and death, and in the process found some amazing truths about the human body and the universe. While his other two brothers, Paul and George had wasted their two million dollars on women, drugs and alcohol, his entire money was still intact. As luck would have it, they all returned back to the Father's kingdom around the same time. While Paul and George came in shame to get a bag of million more and go back to accomplish their missions, Peter walked in with his head high, eyes sparkling, and a heart-warming smile on his face.

The King welcomed all three sons with open arms and listened to their stories with love and patience. He told Paul and George not to worry or be ashamed of what they had done, as life was all a learning experience. If they had now understood and realized what their true mission in England and USA was, then this time around they'll use the money wisely, and not succumb to the artificial pleasures of the senses, but seek true and everlasting pleasure that comes from learning. To Peter he said, I welcome you back into my kingdom, and as now you have turned into a master healer and spiritual master, you'll stay here with me and serve the people with your talents and knowledge.

The story of our journey on earth is very similar to that of Paul, George, and Peter. You may call it the Universe, or God or Creator, it doesn't matter, but that eternal power of creation has set up a marvelous progressive system for our evolution. The human body given to us is the equivalent of the one million dollars the King gave his sons. The majority of us get swayed by our pleasure senses and waste our time on earth, as Paul and George did in England and USA, while totally forgetting our purpose in life. One fine day when the million dollars, that is, the human body, perishes, we will return back home. If we have not completed our mission, another body will be given to come back to Earth and accomplish it. There was no limit on time or money for the three sons, and there is no time frame or the number of human bodies we would need to become masters of our talents.

One fine day, on the path of evolution in this school of life on earth, the realization will eventually dawn upon you to make efforts to find your true identity, get acquainted with your inborn talent and work upon it to become the best you can be. Only then, will you find true eternal success in every single sphere of your life. So why wait for another lifetime, why not do it right now? It's quite possible the work you're currently involved in might be according to the unique talent inside of you. The secret to soaring high in any profession is to consistently work upon yourself by engaging in relevant studies and appropriate training to excel in your line of business. Then the products or services you offer will be nothing but the best. The key is to get into the long run attitude and go beyond the ordinary life of a human being, as your true nature is infinite and nothing short of extraordinary feats and achievements.

To live in accordance with your infinite nature, you first need to protect your million dollars – the human body, by keeping it in perfect health. If you run out of money, it will not be possible to do anything you want in life. Likewise, if you run out of energy and creativity due to health issues, you simply cannot do anything fruitful to fulfil your mission on Earth. The power of creation running through our bodies is directly responsible for all the progress taking place on Earth. The question is, how well are you protecting the medium through which this power moves and creates? You may call it a paradox, but it is not. The human body you live in is a magical powerhouse responsible for all that happens in your life. The internal state of the body affects the external actions in direct proportion. To do things that you may call heavenly or supernatural, your inner body and every single organ needs to function in that manner.

How to tune your body, organs and cells in line with the ways of Nature to make them function in a heavenly and supernatural manner, and ignite the creative powers of the universe running through you, is what we shall explore in the next chapter.

Chapter 5

Go Back to Nature

To go back to Nature, it's important to first understand your true nature. I have talked enough about the importance of knowing your Self, and hope you can now relate to who you really are in this human body. It is equally vital to realize, there is no 'Death' as far as your existence in the universe is concerned. The body you live in has, and will perish from time to time, but not you, as the Spirit has been made to last for eternity. In the same manner, the body too has been made to function for a certain period of time without any problems. As a matter of fact, there existed an age when people lived for 900 years, a fact that is recorded in many books of knowledge. It is said that Noah and many others of that era lived to a healthy fruitful life of 950 years. Since they were well acquainted with the laws of nature, they definitely made good use of them to have long productive years on earth.

Gradually as time went by, we lost touch with ourselves and the eternal knowledge of living in a healthy disease free body for a lifetime. At present the average age is 75 years, but even for these many years the majority cannot live in a healthy and productive manner. The body that was made to function without any problems for 900 years, now seriously begins to malfunction around the age of fifty. From thereon, its survival largely depends on a regular intake of drugs and medications that create havoc with the internal organs, making them weaker with each passing year. Just look around to see how many folks around the age of fifty and beyond take medications to control blood pressure, diabetes, cholesterol, heart disease, and a number of other ailments. Eventually these drugs lead to life threatening problems like Cancer, and then the shockingly painful treatment includes radiation and chemotherapy. I've seen the last days of a cancer patient who went through this; the pain and trauma was so intense, that it's hard to describe in any possible words. So even the 75 years that people spend in the human body are unhealthy, unproductive, and full of pain and suffering. On the other hand, a majority of those who are fortunate to cross the age of eighty or ninety, simply exist as zombies, having lost either their memories, eyesight, general physiological or psychological wellbeing.

Without any doubt the greatest wonder machine on Earth is the human body. It contains amazing instruments known as organs, which no science can replicate. The magical part is that every organ is not only self-healing, but also keeps on re-creating itself indefinitely; be it the heart, liver, kidneys, digestive, or the reproductive system. Since you're the bona-fide owner of this wonder machine, one of your greatest responsibility is to ensure the self-healing and re-creation process goes on in the most efficient manner. The fact is, you are the creator of your very own body, and whatever condition it may be presently in, let there be no illusions in your mind – it's your very own creation. Another fact you should never forget – you have all the creative powers you will ever need to change your body and organs any time you wish to.

The human body has over 37 trillion cells that are responsible for various functions, including healing and regeneration. Every three months, on average, old cells die and new ones take birth. Ancient healing sciences like Ayurveda have long stood by time-tested principles of how the human body degenerates and regenerates by the kind of life an individual lives. They all confirm one basic truth – health and regeneration is the natural state of the body, while disease and degeneration is its un-natural state. Depending upon regular physical activity and proper diet, one can be young and vibrant in every area of their lives even at age one hundred.

To add confirmation to the principles of natural healing sciences, modern medical science has published facts about how long it takes a healthy body to regenerate or grow new organs, skin, and cells. They have discovered that regeneration takes place in two basic steps. First, the old cell matter is channeled to the intestines through the blood stream for elimination with the food waste. Second, new cell matter is created from nutrients found in foods that an individual consumes. These nutrients are absorbed through the intestinal walls into the blood stream, and then distributed to the entire body for the regeneration process to continue unabated. According to their research, new red blood cells are formed every 120 days, new skeleton every 90 days, new brain cells and tissue every 60 days, new stomach lining every 5 days, and a new liver every 45 days.

Our lives on earth are governed by various universal laws, and one important law is the law of sow and reap. This law applies to every area of our life, including regeneration and degeneration of the body. Since new cell matter and the subsequent organ development takes place according to nutrients from the foods we consume, it all depends on the kind of foods we are providing our body. Good foods will obviously provide good nutrients, resulting into good cell matter and good organs. On the other hand, unhealthy foods will undoubtedly provide bad nutrients, resulting into bad cell matter and weak organs. The law of sow and reap plays out perfectly in every segment of our lives. As we are the creators of our body, the creation will happen exactly in accordance with the foods and nutrients we provide our bodies every day. Of course, regular physical exercise, yoga, acupressure, Reiki etc., have their own important benefits in keeping the mind and body fit, but there is definitely no substitute to foods in the regeneration and degeneration processes of the body.

It doesn't matter in what state your body currently is and what state the various organs are at the present moment. Nor does it matter how badly you may have abused the body with wrong foods, drugs and medications. The good news is, the moment you begin to feed the same body with healthy foods, the regeneration process begins to move in the right direction from the nutrients derived from those foods. Change never happens overnight as it is a gradual step by step process, so it is important to understand how this works.

As old cells are replaced by new ones, the change in diet becomes the basic foundation for regeneration. For example, if new red blood cells are formed every 120 days, the nutrients from the good foods will gradually affect the new in-coming cells. It will take three complete cycles of 120 days each for the red blood cells to reach the optimum healthy performance level. For the skeleton, it will be three cycles of 90 days each, and for the liver three cycles of 45 days each. In a similar way all other cells and related organs will be renewed in accordance with a certain time frame.

Nature moves in an extremely orderly manner at a unique consistent pace. Why does it take nine months for a child to be born? Because, that is the required time period for all the organs in the body to develop to the optimum level. At times due to the medical condition or health of the mother, premature delivery takes place. In such cases the newborn is kept in an incubator for the remaining period of pregnancy to provide womb-like conditions for the organs to develop fully. In a similar vein, the regeneration of every organ of the human body takes places according to nature's standard time frame. There's no question of premature delivery where regeneration of your organs is concerned, and there is no incubator in which they can be placed for the remaining time period, in case you cease following your new diet plan and way of life.

To understand the regeneration process of the body clearly, let's compare it to pregnancy. When a woman conceives, the doctor would normally advise her to follow a certain lifestyle, which might be quite different from the routine. For delivering a healthy bouncing baby, her daily diet may include things like, fresh raw vegetables, fruits, nuts, milk, supplements etc. If drinking alcohol or smoking is a part of her daily or weekly activities, she will be advised to stay away from them during the entire term of pregnancy, as they may hamper the growth process and proper organ development of the child. In general, the doctor would recommend various other health measures, like taking in sufficient fresh air and sunshine, keeping calm and staying happy all the time.

During the time of pregnancy, a woman normally forgets about her personal likes and dislikes, and is more concerned about the child developing in her womb. For instance, she may not like to eat raw vegetables, or may have a strong disliking for milk, but if she has been told these are good for the baby, she'll gladly have them without any fuss. She may be fond of having a drink or two in the evenings or weekends, or smoking cigarettes, but during pregnancy she will sacrifice all that to give her best to the life inside of her. This is exactly what you have to do when you're ready to begin the process of regeneration of your cells and organs.

You will have to forget your likes and dislikes and provide good foods to the living and developing organs of your body. In more simpler and straight forward terms, you would have to become pregnant with this truth that you indeed are the creator of your very own body and your organs are very much like a child developing in a womb.

The foods that you have every day are the raw materials of creation. If you are building a home to live in, the same principle applies. The strength and durability of the home would mainly depend on the raw materials used in construction. For example, if inferior materials are used for the foundation, cracks would develop in the walls after a few years. No matter how many times you fix them, they will reappear again and again, until the basic foundational fault is corrected. In a like manner, your diet and way of life are the foundations for the home you live in, which happens to be your body – the biggest wonder on earth. Where a physical home is concerned you have to physically fix the faults when they appear. But with the human body, you only have to provide the right raw materials through foods, and it will automatically fix the faults by renewing your cells and organs.

For several years of my life I wondered how people could enjoy eating raw vegetables. I tried having them a couple of times, but didn't like the taste or texture compared to the cooked foods. Only when I read about the important role they play in regeneration of our cells and organs, did I make an effort to try again. I began eating a bowl of salad before dinner, which contained carrots, cucumbers, tomatoes, cauliflower, radish, kale, broccoli, bell-peppers, and cabbage. As they were all organic, I was truly amazed to find how delicious they were. Every bite was pure heaven, and I simply got hooked on to the crunchiness and the raw feel of this new diet. At that particular time I had no clue about the mind-blowing changes the nutrients from these raw vegetables would do to my cells, organs and overall health. I truly believe it's a wonder that at age 60 my body and the various organs are functioning as they would normally do at age 25.

About five years ago, on the advice of Doctor James Brodsky, a practicing Naturopath and Homeopath in Orange County, California, I did various blood tests as per his recommendations. When the results arrived he was seemingly shocked, as they did not seem to be of a 55 year old, but rather of a 25 year old. I did the same tests in Ghana last year, and Doctor Nortey, a senior medical authority at Korle-Bu Hospital confirmed the same facts. He exclaimed with wonder on his face, "At age 59 your blood tests confirm a timeless truth of nature, that the human body keeps on re-creating itself according to your lifestyle and the foods you have every day. If you continue living in the same manner, even at age 100 all your cells and organs would still be in optimum functional state, and you would be able to do the things you did at age 25 with the same force and vitality."

It is common nowadays that a good majority of men begin to lose their sex drive after age 50, and by the time they cross sixty, it's all over. This is not how it is meant to be, as the human body and all the organs were created to function perfectly up to your last day on earth. It is the life-style and foods that people have, including prescription drugs, medications, smoking and alcohol that leads to the downfall of most men. Medically speaking, men are capable of having children even at age 100, as the body keeps on producing sperm till it dies. In other words, you can be as productive as the produce you provide to your various cells and organs.

The oldest living proof of this is the well documented life of Thomas Parr, who was born in 1483 and died in 1635, at the age of 152 years in England. He was a common agricultural laborer who lived on the produce of the land. Coarse bread, vegetables, cheese, ale, and milk in every form comprised his diet. For the first 80 years of his life he was a bachelor, and when he married, had two children. It is said, when he was 105 years old he was reprimanded by the vicar of Alberbury Parish Church for having an affair and a child out of wedlock. After his first wife died, he married again at the age of 122 years and fathered more children. His wife is known to have said that Thomas was sexually active until the last days of his life. He became a national celebrity when people came to know about his age. In 1635, he was brought to London to meet King Charles I as the oldest living man in history. After that he became a spectacle in England and his portrait was painted by Rubens and Van Dyck, and is now displayed at the National Portrait Gallery in London. When he died at age 152 years and 9 months, William Harvey, the physician who made the discovery about blood circulation, performed a post-mortem on his body and discovered that all the internal organs were in perfect state.

Thomas Parr's diet was directly responsible for his body to have lived for 152 years and his internal organs to be in perfect state up to his last days. As he lived on the produce of the land, he had direct access to raw vegetables and a whole lot of pure milk products, which must have played an instrumental role in the continuous regeneration of his cells and organs in the most optimum manner. No doubt, being a farm laborer required physical work, so exercising most of his body parts daily was natural, which also played a significant role toward his long healthy life.

Today, there is widespread evidence of the role raw vegetables play in contributing toward your health and wellbeing. Medical and health experts have long agreed that people need to eat more vegetables and fruits. Now they have moved a step further by confirming that we need to eat more raw produce. The reason behind this is simple; many of the antioxidants, fiber and other important nutrients are lost in the cooking process. Even the National Cancer Institute recommends 5 servings of vegetables and 3 servings of fruits every day. These foods have disease fighting compounds called phytochemicals, which prevent cell damage and make you look young as you age, and also help to prevent cancer simultaneously.

In general, raw vegetables and fruits are low in fat and

contain a great amount of vitamins and minerals. Green, orange and yellow vegetables are rich sources of iron, calcium, magnesium, potassium, and vitamins A, B, C, and K. They assist the body to develop the capacity to fight against diseases and cancer, and are full of soluble and insoluble dietary fiber, which absorbs excess water in the colon to prevent health issues like constipation and hemorrhoids. According to a research conducted by Maastricht University scientists in 2008, soluble fibers lower the amount of bad cholesterol in the bloodstream, while the insoluble fibers lower cholesterol intake. Another study carried by scientists at the University of California found that raw vegetables contained higher amounts of anti-oxidants, which neutralize free radicals to protect your body cells and boost immune system to lower the risk of cardiovascular disease. Folic acid and beta-carotene found in raw vegetables is necessary for the formation of red blood cells, and slows down the ageing process by greatly reducing the risk of diseases associated with old age.

My personal experience with raw vegetables and the most recent blood tests confirm the above mentioned facts, which are the eternal truths of life on earth. The raw vegetables I initially began having with dinner have now found their way into my morning meal as well. In addition, there is a good serving of fresh fruits I feast upon every morning with an assortment of raw nuts. As Thomas Parr consumed the raw produce of the land and milk products for his body and all organs to be in good functional state for 152 years, I'm doing likewise. The results are there for everyone to see, as my state of health is a living testimonial of how the raw products from nature keep our cells and organs in a continuous state of regeneration. Thomas Parr did physical exercise through farm labor 6 days a week, while I work out in my gym 6 days a week, to give my body the required amount of exercise and keep the organs in the best shape they can be.

One other important element to consider is the number of meals you should have daily. It is not known how many meals Thomas Parr had, but if we revisit the British and European eating patterns of the 15th century, the majority of people had two meals a day. The first meal known as dinner was the heaviest, had in the morning between 9 to 11am, and the evening meal called supper, a little lighter than dinner, between 4 to 6pm. The farming community in North India known as Jat Sikhs have followed a similar meal plan from hundreds of years, and have the strongest genetics and life-span compared to all other tribes in the second most populated nation of the world. During the British rule, they formed over thirty percent of the Indian army, although their population was barely two percent. They accomplished great feats of bravery and made a name for themselves for their courage, strength, and endurance on the battlefield to achieve numerous victories. In direct comparison to the diet of Thomas Parr, they also lived on the produce of the land, ate a lot of raw vegetables and had milk in every form.

I began experimenting with this ancient way of having two meals few years ago to verify if this was better than the five meals recommended by most health professionals. My first meal is around 9am, and is loaded with a vast number of nutrients the body would need to stay active the entire day. The meal typically consists of a large serving of raw vegetable salad with cheese, hummus or salsa, assorted nuts, yogurt, and a large bowl of smoothie prepared with milk and fresh fruits. This meal gives me tremendous energy and keeps the body in high gear for rest of the day. The best part is, I am able to focus on work without having to bother about lunch. It's quite normal that a person becomes lazy after the midday meal and the work output or efficiency is greatly reduced. This being the reason why people are more active in the morning hours, when compared to afternoon. Besides the health benefits of skipping lunch, my productivity and creativity has vastly increased, which obviously means greater overall success in all that I do. The second meal is between 6 to 7pm, and it would normally consist of a raw vegetable salad, lentil soup, cooked cheese or mixed vegetables, and brown rice or wheat bread.

Having experimented with the five and two meals regimen, I find the latter so much more beneficial in several ways. Firstly, it's not easy to follow the five meal plan for people who are actively working. Preparation and taking meals to work is quite a hassle, and then finding time to have them is a great distraction when involved in work. Also, when you're unable to take meals from home, the only choice is eating unhealthy food from outside. Whereas in the two meal program, it's simple to have the morning meal at home before leaving for work, and the evening meal after you return. I am amazed at how fruitful my days have become, as I can accomplish so much more in the same time frame. The kind of high energy people usually have only in the morning hours, I have that for the entire day. While other people look forward to lunch break, I have nothing but the work I do to look forward to.

Our eyes are truly the windows of our soul, through which we see, communicate, and enjoy the wonders of life. When we don't provide the right nourishment and nutrients to our body, along with other organs, the eyes too begin to weaken. The internal state of the organs one cannot see, but the state of eyes becomes easily visible when you begin having problems in reading books, or using a computer etc. I too was no exception as my vision began diminishing around the age of 45. This was the time when my life was taking a complete 180 degree turn, as I had realized the importance of taking care of the physical body I lived in. As I moved ahead in my journey of keeping the body fit and healthy, the vision kept improving.

Besides vision, there are four other important elements that determine the quality of human life on earth. These are – the sense of taste, touch, smell, and hearing. Normally after mid-age the powers of all the five senses begin to lose their strength. Eyeglasses or contact lenses may help you to have a clear vision, while hearing-aids will help you hear better, but what about the sense of touch, taste, and smell? There's no gadget that can improve or maintain the powers of these important senses that facilitate our experience of the true joys of life. In 1760, Immanuel Kant, a famous philosopher, brought forward a very relevant point concerning the importance of our senses. He said that in order to understand the outer extrasensory world, we need to understand our inner sensory world. Each of the five senses are composed of organs having cellular structures that have receptors for specific stimuli, which are linked to the nervous system and the brain. Sight is the most evolved sense modality followed by hearing, touch, taste and smell. People often look for extrasensory experiences externally without realizing these are all internal. If we are doing all the right things to keep our bodies in perfect order, the five senses would work at an optimum level, and every little thing we see, hear, touch, taste, or smell will give us an extrasensory experience.

Today at age 60 not only do I have perfect vision, but the other four senses are also functioning in the most extraordinary manner. Each moment of my life that I am awake is an extrasensory experience, as I can hear distant sounds, and distinct musical notes in songs, which most people cannot. I am able to smell the fragrance of flowers or aroma of foods from far away, while my sense of touch and taste are sensitive in a beautiful way which helps me experience life in its subtleties. You can well imagine what might be the state of all my other internal organs. Am I doing anything supernatural for my body to be in such a heavenly state of health? Did Thomas Parr do anything supernatural to have a perfect body and enjoy the wonders of youth till the ripe age of 152 years? Do you have to do anything supernatural to achieve the same results?

The truth is, no supernatural act is required to have perfect health. The sole requirement of course, is discipline and commitment, with a strong intent to do what is required for the body to be in a continuous state of regeneration. If you've had an unhealthy lifestyle till now, it doesn't matter; if you've abused your body with wrong foods, drugs and medications, it doesn't matter. The moment you change all that and set yourself on the path of improvement, the inception of a new body dawns. It's all up to you as you truly are the 'Master of your Destiny', and the foods you provide your body will become the raw materials for creation of new cells and regeneration of the existing organs.

While constructing a physical home to live in, it's not enough to have the raw materials in hand, as there are many other important aspects that need to be followed to make it fit for living with respect to various other dimensions. Likewise, in the process of regeneration of your existing body you would also need to follow a certain lifestyle for the cells and organs to develop as per your expectations. Going Back to Nature also means going back to a tried and tested way of life. For a seed to grow and blossom to the ultimate capacity the gardener has to provide a fertile soil, sufficient water, the right nutrients, regular clearing of weeds etcetera. As you are the gardener of your body, you would have to do all that. How will you do it? This is what we will explore in the next chapter.

Chapter 6

A New Way of Life

To begin a new way of life, the first step is to accept the responsibility of becoming a Gardener, and the garden in question is your very own body. Creation began from the Garden of Eden, which is considered in scriptures as the purest place on Earth. The Human Body is also called the Temple of God, and should be considered equally pure. If today most people agree that humankind has been gradually destroying the Earth we live on, it's a direct reference to the destruction of the human body. The continuous pollution of planet Earth with all kinds of chemicals is directly due to the state of our bodies. If you're not concerned about the deterioration of your own body due to an unhealthy lifestyle, how much will the destruction of Earth matter to you? To save the Earth, we'll have to save our bodies first. There's no other way, but to take individual responsibility to keep your body clean and chemical free. Whatever a gardener does to keep the garden intact, that's what you have to do. To plant the seed of good health the foremost requirement is fertile soil. Due to your current lifestyle such fertility may not be in existence at this time, but that should not be a problem. If the land within you is infertile, it can be easily turned fertile by a simple age-old practice that has been known to the wise-men since time immemorial.

This timeless practice is called – Fasting, and it not only helps in clearing toxins from the body, but also greatly aids in rejuvenating all the internal organs. Prophets and learned men of every generation have laid great emphasis on practicing this cleansing process regularly. In fact, the practice of fasting has been embodied into religious practices of every world religion. For Muslims, there's a 30 day mandatory fasting once a year during the month of Ramadan, when they can only eat before dawn and after sunset. In Christianity, there's a 40 day fast every year during the Lent period, beginning on Ash Wednesday and ending on Easter. Although the rules may vary, but in general, members can have one meal in the evening, but they must avoid meats, meat products, fish, eggs, and alcohol. Besides this annual fast, some Christian sects follow a weekly fast, when they must abstain from eating foods for 24 hours. In the Hindu religion there are various monthly and yearly fasts, but as a regular practice fasting is recommended once a week for 24 hours. All these religions highlight the same theme that fasting will bring you closer to God by making your body pure and help to receive his favors abundantly.

The scientific world whole-heartedly agrees to this religious theme that fasting helps to make the human body pure by eliminating toxins, wastes, and dangerous poisons that make you sick and age prematurely. The 15th century physician, Paracelsus, highlighted that fasting was the greatest remedy and the physician within. While Hippocrates, the Father of Medicine, said: "Everyone has a physician inside him or her; we just have to help it in its work. The natural healing force within each one of us is the greatest force in getting well. Our food should be our medicine. Our medicine should be our food. But to eat when you are sick is to feed your sickness."

Fasting is indeed the ultimate detoxifying method to enhance the miraculous self-healing processes of the human body to keep you healthy, young, and vibrant throughout the living years. Have you ever noticed when a dog or a cat is not feeling well, they stop eating for a day or two. The same animal instinct is also a part of the human physiology, but the majority of us hardly pay any heed to such a vital aspect of our wellbeing. Our body speaks to us all the time, but most people rarely listen to it, and at the first sign of any discomfort or ailment they usually head to a physician or pharmacist to find a cure with the help of modern drugs and medications. Hippocrates never prescribed such drugs. For every disease in the acute stage he always advocated a simple water fast.

In general, fasting is like a medical surgery without any operation or incisions to cut you open and take out accumulated toxins, damaged or diseased tissues, waste buildups, cancerous growths and fat deposits through your skin, blood stream, liver, and kidneys. Nowadays due to an increased aesthetic awareness and pressure to look good, people opt for surgeries to remove fat deposits from their body. But these deposits, toxins, and buildups are the main culprits that lead to every kind of sickness and life-threatening health ailments. No surgery, except fasting, can permanently remove or eradicate them. The learned men or prophets of various religions were well acquainted with the science behind the human body. They also knew how difficult it was for the masses to follow a disciplined way of life to care for their bodies and be in good health. So they incorporated fasting into their religions as a compulsory practice for people to follow for winning favors from God, or as a sign of being a good Muslim, Hindu, or Christian.

Today, a great number of people, worldwide, follow the religious fasting, but the majority undertake only the yearly fasts. Muslims fast for 30 days during Ramadan and Christians do it for 40 days during the Lent period, while Hindus have various yearly, monthly, and weekly fasts. It should be noted that Islam promises exceptional rewards to those who fast once every week. Some Christian sects also advocate a weekly 24 hour fast, while a segment of Hindus fast once or twice a week.

Toxins, wastes, cancerous growths and fat deposits are building up in our bodies every day. If one has to wait for a year to do a 30 or 40 day fast, it would be too late to cleanse the body and avoid sickness or disease. Is it possible that you eat only once a year for 30 or 40 days, and then stay hungry for the remaining months? Can you possibly survive in such a scenario? If not, then how can the human body survive without elimination of dangerous toxins and waste buildups for 11 months? The rewards that religions promise through regular fasting are the rewards of good health. Once you fast every week, the accumulated wastes and toxins will be eliminated the same week and not carried over. No toxins – no disease, this is the simple law of nature which the modern medical establishment duly endorses.

To enjoy vibrant health at any age a weekly 24 hour fast is most essential. The best way is to do it the Hippocratic way by undertaking a water fast. Hippocrates practiced medicine in the 4th century B.C., and today modern medical doctors take the Hippocratic Oath upon graduation. A part of that oath highlights: "I will prevent disease whenever I can, for prevention is preferable to cure." What did he really do to not only prevent, but also treat disease, which today's doctors don't? He prescribed a simple water fast; and if you follow this prescription you can prevent disease not whenever you can, but every single week.

The most ideal day of fasting is Monday, as most people indulge in high calorie-loaded delicacies and desserts over the weekends. All the garbage that has collected in your gut should be cleared off as a new week begins. If your last meal on Sunday is at 7pm, the 24 hour fast should begin right after, and end on Monday at 7pm. Basically what that means is – you'll not have any meal when you wake up Monday morning, until 7pm. Think about it, is that really a difficult thing to do? As this will be a water fast, all you need to do is to drink water at regular intervals. If you can have a glass every hour, that would be the ultimate water fast, as it will flush your entire body from various toxins that may have accumulated over the past week. During a fast the body is free from the regular work of digestion, so it gets down to clear all undesirable elements, while the water acts as a booster and detergent in the cleansing process.

Initially you may find it a little difficult to get accustomed to fasting, but the human body is programmed in such a unique fashion that it easily adapts to any change. The first day of fasting would be the most difficult, as you'll really feel hungry at times, and it may seem your energy levels have hit rock-bottom. There will certainly be a strong urge to break the fast and eat something. This will indeed be the most critical time when you would have to stand strong as a gardener working to reclaim the lost garden. After all, you are the master of your destiny and there is virtually nothing beyond your reach. It's the 'will' that matters, not only to initiate fasting into your life, but also in every other area related to your success as an individual entity in the grander design of the universe.

The second Monday of fasting will be a lot easier than the first, and this trend will continue week after week. It takes three months for the human body to completely adapt to any new change in lifestyle. Once you reach that milestone, fasting will become a natural part of you. The imprint of fasting will be all over your cells and organs by then, and you will no longer have any hunger-pangs or feel low on energy, as the body adjusts its requirements accordingly. Rather, you'll have more energy on the day of fasting and be able to accomplish greater tasks compared to other days.

I personally look forward to my weekly fast with great eagerness, as it is such a heavenly feeling to have the body cleansed and detoxified from all the toxins. I feel so light and super-charged and my level of productivity on the day of fasting is truly outstanding. Over the years I have had the opportunity of witnessing the yearly fasts of people from various religions. In most cases the energy levels of these groups are at their lowest ebb on the fasting days and hardly any important tasks are accomplished. Some of them would just go and sleep for most part of the day, as they were unable to control the hunger pangs. This scenario is absolutely normal when you fast only once a year, but with a regular weekly fast the situation transforms entirely, and your productivity improves profoundly.

Fasting is the first essential step to begin a new way of life by cleansing and detoxifying your body every week. The water you'll have on the day of fasting will greatly help to create the required fertile conditions for the seeds to bear good fruit. In fact, you should make it a regular habit to drink enough water every day. It does not have to be every hour, but there should be a minimum of five to seven glasses daily. After fasting has turned your inner garden fertile, the next step is to sow the seeds that would lead to good health.

What really are the seeds of good health? The foods you have daily are the seeds that determine the condition of your overall health and every single organ. What better seed can there be than the raw produce of the land that Thomas Parr had – the oldest healthy living man in modern history? So twice a day before the main meal you should have a decent-sized salad serving consisting of raw organic vegetables. You can select from a wide variety that is available, depending upon where you live, and according to your personal taste. These could be tomatoes, cucumbers, cabbage, cauliflower, red, yellow and green bell-peppers, carrots, sweet potatoes, yam, broccoli, radish, green salad leafs, avocado, etcetera. The best way is to slice them into thin strips or cut into little pieces. With each serving your taste buds will be delighted with the exotic flavor of a variety of raw vegetables. The crunchiness of cabbage, bell-pepper, carrots and the wholesome ingredients of tomatoes and cucumbers will provide a mouth-watering experience that not only whets, but curbs the appetite to disallow any excessive eating. You can add some hummus, coconut/peanut paste, salsa or any salad dressing to get a curry like effect. If anyone has a problem eating raw vegetables, simply place them in a pan and sauté on the fire for 3 to 4 minutes.

It is important that the raw vegetables are organic and free from pesticides, and do not originate from GMO seeds. If you live in the USA or Europe it would not be difficult to lay hands on organic produce as food awareness is gradually rising. People are increasingly becoming health conscious about what they eat and farmers are gradually shifting to organic methods and non-GMO seeds. Food awareness is also on the rise in many other countries in the Far East, Latin-America and parts of Africa, where farmers are fighting to stop the entry of GMO seeds into their agriculture chain.

GMO stands for Genetically Modified Organisms, and these seeds are mainly produced by a company called Monsanto by manipulation of extremely deadly viruses and bacteria. Their main goal is to monopolize the world market in all aspects of food, seeds, and related chemicals. These seeds are patented and are said to provide a greater yield than regular seeds, and have to be used with their patented herbicide known as Roundup, which contains an extremely dangerous ingredient 'Glyphosate'.

An independent research done by Anthony Samsel, a science consultant and Dr. Stephanie Seneff, a research scientist at the Massachusetts Institute of Technology reveals how Glyphosate destroys human health and greatly aids in the development of multiple chronic diseases and conditions, such as: Autism, Alzheimer's, Parkinson's, Colitis, Infertility, Obesity, Depression, Chronic diarrhea, Cardiovascular disease, and Cancer. Their report was published in the journal, Entropy, highlighting the issue of glyphosate residues found in the most common foods, like, corn, sugar, wheat, and soy, as to how this dangerous herbicide produced by Monsanto under their patented brand 'Roundup' enhances the damaging effects of other food-borne chemical residues and toxins to disrupt the normal bodily functions and induce disease.

Meanwhile, Monsanto obviously claims Roundup is completely harmless to both humans and animals. You may wonder why animals are included in their claim. Most people are totally unaware that even animals are fed these GMO foods laden with this dangerous herbicide. So in case you eat meats, there is a double dose of Roundup finding its way into your body to cause even greater harm. To justify this is harmless, Monsanto claims that the mechanism of action it uses to kill weeds is the shikimate pathway, which is absent in all animals. What they fail to tell you is that the shikimate pathway is very much present in bacteria, which is the key to understand how it causes intense harm to both humans and animals. The bacteria in our bodies outnumber the cells by a ratio of ten to one, which means for every cell there are ten microbes, and all of them have the shikimate pathway. So the mechanism of action, which Monsanto claims that it uses to kill weeds, will also kill your healthy cells.

What Monsanto as the leader of the modern biotech industry has done to amass unimaginable amounts of wealth is to turn food into poison. Forget about the harmful effects of Roundup, the genetic alteration of a crop itself leads to major health problems. With all the GMO crops there are two hazardous factors to contend with; the genetically modified seeds, and the toxins from Roundup. In their quest to control the world food market they have left nothing untouched; from mustard to okra, rice, soya, cauliflower, oil, sugar, corn, potatoes, wheat, and many other crops. Forget about vegetables, rice, or oil, even meats are laden with these harmful ingredients as animals are being fed the same diets. Once they convince the farmers or the relevant authorities of any nation, the route to amassing wealth forever is established, as the GMO seeds can be owned as their property and royalties collected for an indefinite period. The farmers will have to depend on them for every seed of every crop they grow. If Monsanto control the seed, they control not only the food markets, but the populations of the world. This is a power beyond any wildest insane imagination and much more powerful than controlling the human race through guns, nuclear arsenals or dictatorial regimes.

The story of Monsanto's GMO's began in the highly elite circles of American politics, where they got its way by exerting undue influence over policymakers. One of their Attorney, Michael R. Taylor, was first appointed as deputy commissioner for policy in 1991 at the FDA – the US Food and Drug Administration that is responsible for all food approvals. Then he was moved to USDA – United States Department of Agriculture in 1994 as Administrator of the Food Safety and Inspection Service. During his tenure at both places he made crucial decisions that led to the approval of GMO foods and crops without proper testing as per the laid out rules and regulations. After completing this assigned work at FDA and USDA, this gentleman returned to Monsanto in 1996 as the company's vice president for public policy. Then in the year 2000, he published two important documents on which USA aid for African agriculture is based to promote GMO seeds.

The surprising element is that these genetically modified foods and crops were adopted without proper testing and consumer labeling, in spite of serious unanswered questions over their safety. Monsanto's influence stretched to such an extent that the US Food and Drugs Agency completely ignored warnings of their own scientists about how these genetically modified crops could cause great harm to human health. Their connections and political clout was clearly demonstrated when President Obama appointed the same Michael R. Taylor in January 2010 as Deputy Commissioner for Foods at FDA. The plot further thickened when Obama signed the short-term spending bill in March 2013 to prevent Government from shutting down. Neatly slipped inside this bill was section 735 called the Farmer Assurance Provision or the Monsanto Protection Act, which would allow USDA to approve planting of GMO crops even if the judiciary declared them unsafe for human health.

On their website Monsanto claims to be an Agriculture company, who aims to help farmers produce healthier food to meet the needs of a growing population, to protect and preserve this planet we call home, and to help improve lives everywhere. But these claims are far away from actual reality and their past history, and to stifle concerns about their products they've always indulged in misleading advertisements, concealment of scientific evidence, and in many cases, bribery. The real story of Monsanto began in 1901, when the company was founded by a chemist. It went on to become one of the largest chemical companies of the 20th century with their bestselling and most controversial product known as PCBs, which were chemically created oils used worldwide as coolants and lubricants for electrical equipment. For over four decades Monsanto minted millions of dollars from PCBs, until they were banned in the USA in 1977 and all over the world in the early 80's.

The ban came after years of protest from various circles and groups, due to which the relevant authorities in the USA and other countries were forced to conduct tests to determine how harmful the PCBs were on human health and the environment. It's not as if Monsanto didn't know how harmful they were, as clear documented evidence has been unearthed to confirm they hid decades of pollution and harm inflicted on the people and the environment of the town where these dangerous products were produced. In January 2002, the Washington Post published an article highlighting how Monsanto polluted and poisoned the city of Anniston in Alabama, where they produced PCBs at a local factory. The article illustrates a long chain of deceit, greed, and secrecy that was maintained for over 40 years to produce this highly toxic product. During this period Monsanto regularly poured toxic waste into Anniston creek and offloaded millions of pounds of PCBs into open-pit landfills.

In 1966, their managers found that fish in that creek were turning belly-up, spurting blood and shedding skin, but they kept this secret. Later, they found fish in another creek with 7,500 times the legal permissible level of PCBs, but Monsanto decided there was no reason to use expensive means to limit discharge of the toxic waste. To stifle down the concern of the managers, they eventually hired a biologist named Denzel

Ferguson to conduct studies around Anniston. Ferguson came in with tanks full of bluegill fish and submerged them at various locations. All the fish turned on their sides within 10 minutes and were dead in less than 4 minutes. It was as if they had been dumped into battery acid. Ferguson concluded that the waste water flowing from the Monsanto plant was extremely toxic and represented a potential source of danger to children, and he advised them to clean up the creeks and stop dumping further waste. But Monsanto did not do that, even though the warnings continued. Eventually they were forced to spend over 40 million dollars on cleanup efforts and over 700 million on legal settlements on various lawsuits, which uncovered documents that revealed the story of secret corporate actions to hide the gross damage these chemicals could cause to the environment and human health.

In 1967, a group of Swedish scientists demonstrated beyond any reasonable doubt that PCBs were a big threat to the global environment. They clearly identified traces of PCBs in the entire food chain, in birds and fish, even in children's hair. So what did Monsanto do in face of such clear cut evidence? Their simple response was to prepare for a media war to rubbish these reports and findings. One of their medical director wrote a memo asking if there was anything he could do to make sure their business was not affected by this evil publicity.

In 1968, PCBs were discovered in California's wildlife, setting off a huge debate and controversy in the USA. This is when Monsanto officials began talking about damage control, as the evidence on their impact on the environment was more than substantial. One official wrote that it was only a matter of time before the regulatory agencies will be looking down our throats. Another official wrote that we should begin to protect ourselves and limit further releases of PCBs.

In 1969, Monsanto appointed an Ad-Hoc Committee to look into these controversies surrounding their most profitable product PCBs. According to the minutes of the first meeting the Committee's two main objectives were to protect the image of the corporation, and to allow continued sales and profits. But they realized the situation indeed looked bleak, as chemical traces had been found across the USA in fish, oysters, shrimp, bald eagles, and even in milk. Their status as a serious pollutant was certain, and it seemed to be just a matter of time before the authorities took some concrete action. One option they had was to stop production immediately, and the other was to sell as much possible as long as they could. The committee instead went for what they called the responsible approach to gradually phase out the PCBs, but only once the company had developed alternatives. They also urged more studies to be undertaken to find evidence that they were not harmful to the environment, as this had turned into a raging topic in the national media, while members of congress were calling for hearings.

Till 1977 Monsanto kept producing PCBs as the federal law banning them did not take effect till 1979. Various tests that linked them to cancers, birth defects, diabetes, thyroid problems and a variety of immune disorders, were totally ignored by the company in their quest not to lose even one dollar of their business. They greatly profited from over 40 years of monopoly on PCB production in USA and world-wide, and eventually battled with all their might to protect that even long after PCBs were declared as global pollutants. In fact, the PCBs were also used in paints, adhesives, bread wrappers, and deep-fat fryers, without the knowledge of the consumers. Once known as the miracle chemicals, they were eventually declared as cancerous and banned by the EPA and the World Health Organization.

The Ad-Hoc committee that Monsanto set up in 1969 recommended the responsible approach to gradually phase out the PCBs, but only once the company had developed alternatives. The gradual phase continued till 1977, while the company was seriously working on alternatives to continue filling up their coffers. A lot of thinking and planning must have ensued behind closed doors to come up with a new product to enrich the shareholders. It must have been some super brainstorming sessions that gave birth to a phenomenal idea of investing into research of GMO seeds. With genetically modified seeds, not only would they turn into an agriculture company and improve their image, but also have control of the world's food markets. But the problem was, they were a chemical company since inception and all they knew and did during their 80 years of existence was to produce and profit from chemicals. To look for a replacement chemical of their most profitable product PCBs must have been their most important agenda.

In 1983, Monsanto announced they had succeeded in genetically modifying a plant cell, and field trials of genetically modified crops were done in 1987. This made them the pioneers in applying the biotechnology industry business model to agriculture. In this model companies invest in research and development, and then recover not only the investments, but make massive profits with the use and enforcement of patents. Monsanto was well acquainted with this model and used it successfully for over 80 years in their chemical business. Now with the ban on PCBs, they diverted most of that business through mergers and buyoffs to become the biggest GMO seed company. Their seed patenting model became a direct threat to customary farming practices of sharing, reusing, and developing plant varieties. Once a farmer buys their seeds, he would have to buy them again and again every year.

For as long as agriculture has been in practice, farmers have saved seeds from their current harvest to sow the following year, but Monsanto has changed this natural course of nature. They have succeeded in patenting their GMO seeds, just like patented drugs and other commercial products, and farmers are prohibited from saving seeds for future use. If they do save them, Monsanto tracks them down and prosecutes to set an example and warn others. They have launched a permanent war against farmers to protect their way of business. A farmer in the USA was forced to pay over USD 80,000 through a Supreme Court ruling for using their

GMO seeds saved from an earlier harvest. From thousands of cases that they ruthlessly pursue, a great number are settled out of court, as farmers are afraid to take any stand against them. Not only farmers, they also track the dealings of seed sellers and seed cleaners to grab patent violators, and many a times innocent people are made to pay huge fines. The company collected over USD 160 million till 2007 in out of court settlements from farmers and dealers who could not afford to take a stand against this giant multi-national.

The fact is that GMO crops cannot be contained in one farm, and it's easy for them to spread through winds and cross pollination to the adjoining farms, where conventional farming may be in practice. Rather than being sued for contaminating such farms, Monsanto has done the opposite by suing those farmers for unlicensed crops growing in their fields. Many such farmers ended up losing their farms, but one Canadian farmer, Percy Schmeiser, refused to tolerate such injustice and fought back. For over 40 years he had grown canola on his farm using his own seeds, saved from the previous harvest. In 1998 Monsanto sued him for USD 400,000 when more than 320 hectares of his farmland was found to be contaminated with their GMO canola. He countersued them for trespassing, accusing him of illegal acts, contamination of his crops with GMO plants, and for complete disregard of the environment by introducing such crops without proper controls and containment. This landmark case is featured in a documentary film 'David versus Monsanto', which can be viewed on YouTube. After a decade long battle Percy Schmeiser eventually won, when Monsanto agreed to settle out of court and pay all cleanup costs.

Besides using such mafia-like tactics to control the world seed market, another important factor highlights their true intentions to profit from chemicals. Before the worldwide ban on PCBs, GMO seeds were not the only thing Monsanto planned to invest in. Being the largest chemical company for over 80 years, their fortunes came through chemicals. So how could they leave the chemical business just because their bestselling PCBs were banned? There had to be a new chemical product to replace the PCBs that would go hand in hand with the GMO seeds to generate multiple profits. After the ban and the huge controversies regarding the extensive damage caused to the environment and to the people for four decades, changing their image was most important. By claiming to become an agricultural company with an aim to help farmers produce healthier food to meet the needs of a growing population was more of an eyewash to repair their chemically-tainted image. In actual fact, they had already launched their replacement product Roundup in 1974 with their patented chemical, glyphosate. The GMO seeds were then genetically engineered to tolerate high doses of Roundup by making them immune to this dangerous chemical.

Monsanto indeed planned their transition with great precision. They invented glyphosate and today are the largest producer of herbicides through their Roundup products. The genetically modified seeds are immune to these herbicides, which means, farmers can freely spray as much as required to kill the weeds. Using their extensive network and close contacts with regulatory agencies, Roundup has been approved worldwide, but concerns over its harmful effects on human beings, animals, and the environment have remained in direct comparison to the harmful effect of PCBs. In fact, if you look at the actual scenario, nothing has really changed. Monsanto now claims to be an agriculture company, but still produces the largest selling chemical glyphosate under the brand name Roundup, which they seemingly claim is totally safe. For over 40 years the same company claimed PCBs, that were eventually banned worldwide, were safe too. So how can they be trusted this time around, especially when evidence of damage from these new chemicals is fast emerging? In March 2015, the International Agency for Research on cancer classified glyphosate as cancerous. In view of this finding environment officers in California have issued a notice of intent to place a cancer warning on Roundup.

The study of what happened in Argentina is a good case example of what is happening with GMO seeds and its related chemicals. Monsanto convinced the farmers and agricultural authorities to focus on soybean production, which helped turn this nation into the world's third-largest soybean producer. But the chemicals associated with the genetically modified seeds were not only confined to the agriculture fields. They also contaminated homes, schools, and drinking water, and became responsible for a major increase in multiple health problems. In the farming communities cancer rates have been found to be four times higher than the national average. Since the launch of GMO seeds, chemical spraying has increased eightfold from 9 million gallons to 84 million currently. As Argentina does not apply any national standards for such chemicals and allows the provinces to enforce their own regulations, Monsanto's Roundup products are being used eight to ten times more per acre, when compared to the use in USA. Imagine the amount of profits Monsanto derives from the sale of not only the seeds, but also their major chemical – Roundup, at the expense of the health of people and damage to the environment.

Argentina was best known for its grass-fed beef, but all that has changed since Monsanto introduced their patented GMO seeds and chemicals in 1996. They had assured the farmers that these seeds and chemicals will greatly increase and enhance crop yields and lower the amount of pesticide use. Initially, agrochemical use did decline, but then it bounced back ten-folds as pests became resistant to these new chemicals. In addition, their claims about increased yields with the genetically modified seeds are not backed by any tested or proven results. In fact, many studies have found that there is not much difference in crop yields with GMO seeds, when compared to the regular seeds used in conventional farming.

As was the case with Monsanto's PCBs during their four decades of world dominance, the same alarming patterns of intense harm to human health and the environment are fast emerging with these seeds and chemicals. Some of the note-worthy cases in our study of Argentina are worth looking at with a deeper perspective. A farm worker who was never properly trained in the use of pesticides is a living skeleton at age 47, hardly able to eat or walk without assistance. A lady lost her newborn due to kidney failure, and her complaint led to the first criminal conviction in Argentina for chemical spraying. A government study found extremely high levels of agrochemical contamination in the soil and water, and majority of the people tested had high traces of pesticides in their blood. Birth defects have increased significantly and doctors have warned that these pesticides could be the reason behind growing health issues in the nation's vast farm belt. The great change in how agriculture is now done has brought in an even greater change in disease patterns. From a healthy society during the times of conventional farming, the modern genetic farming introduced by Monsanto has gradually increased the rates of birth defects, cancer, and many other diseases rarely seen before.

A study conducted by a biologist at the University of Buenos Aires confirmed that even a low dose of glyphosate injected into embryos caused similar spinal defects in frogs and chickens, which doctors are finding in the farming communities. As they did with the negative reports on PCBs for years, Monsanto rebutted these results saying these tests should be done on live animals, and that injecting embryos was less reliable and less relevant for human risk assessments. In a similar way, they have totally disregarded and discredited the other independent research which revealed how glyphosate destroys human health and greatly aids in the development of multiple chronic diseases and conditions, such as: Autism, Alzheimer's, Parkinson's, Colitis, Infertility, Obesity, Depression, Chronic diarrhea, Cardiovascular disease, and Cancer.

Monsanto's marketing strategy and manipulative persuasion projecting their products as environmental friendly, high yielding and beneficial for health is nothing new, as this is what they did for over 40 years. Knowing fully well the extent of damage their PCBs caused to human health and the environment, they consistently denied the facts and hid vital information from the public. Once again it is the same story that's getting repeated with GMO seeds and the deadly chemical Roundup, and this time the goal is to control the entire seed and agrochemical market of the world. Using under-hand tactics that involve lobbying and bribery, they've been able to take their seeds and chemicals into every country they possibly could. They entered India and introduced their Bt cotton seeds, which due to the eventual high cost and lower yields led to farmers succumbing to suicide after facing increased debt. Monsanto entirely misrepresented the profitability of these seeds, which caused farmers to suffer heavy losses. For one kilogram of regular seeds, which can be used the next season, the cost was INR 7 – about 10 cents, while for one kilogram of Bt seeds, which they have to buy every season, the cost was INR 2000 – about USD 30. The incidence of farmer suicides in 2011 and

2012 was extremely severe among Bt cotton farmers, and a report by the Indian Council of Agricultural Research in 2012 directly linked the suicides to the high cost and decline in the performance of Bt cotton. One state in India banned Bt cotton in 2012 and so did Hawaii in 2013.

Monsanto's underhand tactics were fully exposed when the US Department of Justice filed a Prosecution Agreement in 2005, and they agreed to pay a USD 1.5 million fine upon admitting to violations of the Foreign Corrupt Practices Act, by way of false entries into their books and records. They also admitted that one of their senior manager had directed a consulting firm to give a USD 50,000 bribe to a high level official of Indonesia's environment ministry. The bribe was in relation to a favorable assessment of their GMO seeds and chemicals. They further made disclosures of paying bribes to a number of other senior officials between 1997 and 2002. All these admissions truly expose how they conduct their business to control the food production and continue selling these dangerous seeds and chemicals. If their seeds are indeed as good as they claim and the Roundup chemicals as harmless as they advertise, what would be the need to bribe high ranking officials to provide favorable reports for them?

Monsanto has been fined and penalized several times over false advertising in various parts of the world. In 1996, they had to withdraw their ads on the orders of the Attorney General of New York. The ads claimed that Roundup was safer than table salt and practically nontoxic. In 1999, they apologized to the UK Advertising Standards Authority for making misleading, unproven and wrong scientific claims about their products. In 2001, consumer rights campaigners in France filed a case against them for misleading the public on the environmental impacts of Roundup, when the European Union had classified its main ingredient glyphosate as dangerous and toxic. Subsequently, they were convicted for false advertising in 2007 and fined EUR 15,000. In 2012, a Brazilian court ordered them to pay a fine of USD 250,000 for false advertising related to the benefits of GMO soya seeds and the chemical Roundup. The federal prosecutor claimed that Monsanto had misrepresented the amount of herbicide required for these seeds, and the goal behind such false advertising was to prepare the market for the purchase of their genetically modified seeds and Roundup. The presiding judge condemned Monsanto and termed the advertisement as abusive and misleading propaganda.

The truth about the hidden agenda and goals of Monsanto is fast becoming public, but as they did with their cancerous PCBs, the same tactics and manipulation are being defiantly used with the influence of money and political connections. They continue to lobby the US Congress, the U.S. Department of Agriculture, and foreign diplomats and officials, about regulations that would affect the production of GMO crops. Every year they spend millions on such initiatives to continue expand their business at the expense of human, animal, and environmental health.

GMO food labeling has been adopted by over 60 countries

as mandatory, but due to Monsanto's political connections and influence it is not required in the USA. In 2012, California voters wanted to pass Proposition 37, which would have made it legal for GMO foods to be labeled, so that consumers are aware of what they are buying. Such labeling would have had gross effects on the sales of their GMO seeds and chemicals. Monsanto fought with all their might spending over USD 8 million with false and misleading advertisements, and the sad part is, they succeeded. Proposition 37 was defeated by 53% voters, who got influenced with their wrongful claims. Although, the silver lining that 48% voters voted in favor of this bill cannot be ignored. This is a clear and positive indication that consumer awareness is on the rise about the foods people consume in the USA. In spite of this proposition not being able to pass, numerous manufacturers have begun labeling their products as non-GMO. Whole-Foods, one of America's largest chain for health foods, has committed to have all their products properly labeled by 2018.

With the amount of money available to Monsanto in their coffers from making cancerous chemicals since 1901 and now GMO's, they're leaving no stone unturned to protect their business interests at any cost. In partnership with the food companies they spent over USD 30 million in lobbying to have the DARK Act passed by the US House of Representatives in July 2015 by a 275-150 vote. If this bill is further passed by the Senate to be enforced as a law, it would bar the Food and Drug Administration from introducing mandatory labeling of GMO foods and ban all fifty states from doing the same, even if voters demand labeling through a ballot measure. It would also forbid the states from making it illegal to label GMO foods as natural and keep Americans in the dark to what they are actually consuming, which will pose a serious threat to their long-term health.

In spite of all their lobbying and money spending, food awareness is rapidly increasing all across the world, and consumers are waking up and taking a stand against Monsanto, who have shown absolute disregard for human, animal, and environmental health. In 2013, protesters rallied in 52 countries and 436 cities against them. In Buenos Aires and other cities in Argentina protesters carried signs that read 'Monsanto-Get out of Latin America'. In Los Angeles demonstrators waved signs 'Real Food 4 Real People' and 'Label GMOs, It is Our Right to Know'.

In many places GMO seeds are being gradually pushed out and organic farming is rapidly taking over. In Hawaii, Mayor Billy Kenoi signed Bill 113 into law in December 2013 to ban GMO crops on Big Island. He said that the law signals the county's desire to encourage community based farming and demonstrate deep respect for our land, and to protect our natural resources. In November 2014, Hawaii's Maui County passed a similar law to ban cultivation of GMO crops. Monsanto spent over USD 8 million to first defeat the voter measure, but after that failed, they filed a lawsuit in a federal court in Honolulu to block the law and invalidate the voter approved measure.

It is difficult to imagine and comprehend Monsanto's

unethical protection of solely their business interests, that too at the cost of life, health and the environment. What they did for over 40 years with PCB's which were proven to be cancerous and banned, is being repeated in a new marketing gimmick in the form of GMO and Roundup. While, more than half of the countries that form the European Union have banned GMO cultivation and many other nations either have, or are on the way to similar action. These include: Australia, New-Zealand, Brazil, Philippines, Thailand, Venezuela, Russia, Egypt, Algeria, and Saudi Arabia, who have placed a ban on all importation and distribution of GMO foods.

Looking at the prospects of a diminished market share, Monsanto is frantically pushing their GMO technology into other countries. They are making massive efforts through strong lobbying of international donors, such as the IMF, World Bank, and USAID, to introduce their seeds into Africa, in particular Ghana, where the Plant Breeder's Bill has been on debate in the Parliament since 2013. As awareness is rising on this issue, a large section of farmers and activists have been protesting to stop the taking over of their natural agricultural practices. This bill has been rightly dubbed 'Monsanto Law', and is nothing short of a complete takeover of Ghana's agriculture from the hands of small scale farmers to the producers of GMO seeds. If this bill is passed, not only will it spell doom for Ghana as an independent nation, but for all of Africa, as it will wipe out small farmers from business and place the health and survival of an entire continent at stake.

While the bill was still under debate, the Ghana Parliament passed the Biosafety Act 831, which permitted introduction of GMO technology, and confined field trials of rice, cowpea and cotton have been underway in Ashanti and three regions in the North. The normal course of action after the field trials should have been to evaluate the GMO produce with regards to the cost, safety concerns, long-term impacts on farmers and the environment, and compare with the current traditional farming. It is only then a fair and transparent analysis could have been made. But the concerned authorities bypassed this extremely crucial and critical procedure, including the rules governing the Biosafety Act, and announced the commercial release of GMO cowpeas and rice on to the Ghanaian market. This scenario is no different than what happened in the USA, when the FDA approved GMO seeds without proper testing against the backdrop of negative reports about their safety and health concerns from their own scientists. To block this dangerous move, FSG (Food Sovereignty Ghana), who have been on the forefront in this battle against the introduction of GMO seeds and the Plant Breeder's Bill, filed a case in the Accra High Court to place an injunction on the release of these GMO products. The case has been adjourned to a future date, and till then a temporary ban remains on the release.

The elected leaders, officers of regulatory agencies, and members of parliament in all countries in Africa, Far East, and Latin America, where Monsanto is pushing their GMO technology, should take guidance and follow the example set by the people and leaders in Hawaii and other nations who have banned GMO crops. So many people from so many countries are joining hands to successfully ban such dangerous cultivation, and demonstrate deep respect for their land to preserve and protect the natural resources. Inspiration should be drawn from them and every true citizen of his country should join hands to protect their nation from being polluted with these crops and pesticides.

GMO crops are killing pollinating bees, butterflies and birds, and this is a well-known and documented fact. Imagine what will happen if bees become extinct. Not only will the human race be deprived of the benefits of honey and pollinating, our basic survival will be at stake. A beekeeper in New York was forced to sell his 112-acre farm as all his bees were dead. In 2007, he realized the bees were not laying eggs and turning queen-less, and gradually 90 percent of his hives became empty. He found that he was not the only one facing this issue, as beekeepers all over USA and Europe were facing the same problem. Eventually, scientists in France discovered the reason behind these deaths. The bees were dying and becoming extinct due to neonics, a common insecticide being used in genetically engineered farming, and the European Union banned their use after this discovery became public. It may shock you to know that every GMO corn and soybean seed is coated with neonics. In the USA, presently 90 percent of corn and soy are GMO and have this insecticide in them – the reason behind the bees dying. A USDA study in 2012 found neonics in 22 percent of cherry tomatoes, 30 percent of cauliflower, and 25 percent of bell-peppers. While another study by the FDA found neonics in 29 percent of baby food.

It is important to understand why this is happening and how bees pollinate. Pollination is a process when pollen is transferred from the male to female part of the plant. Bees are the ultimate pollinators because they collect pollen to feed their younger ones, and while moving from plant to plant, transfer it from the male to female part. This is their everyday routine that culminates into the most effective natural mode of cross-pollination. It is the ultimate give and take phenomenon God or Nature has put in place. The bees get their pollen, while the plants pollinate to give their utmost yield, and both acts become responsible for the foods on our tables. But companies like Monsanto have placed these dangerous neonics and many other genetically engineered compounds into their GMO seeds that are not only killing bees, but also transferring those chemicals into other non-GMO crops through pollination.

A recent report indicated that 47 million people now have dementia, and these numbers are expected to double every 20 years. According to the World Health Organization, there are 7.7 million new cases every year. People with dementia primarily suffer from memory loss, and also have problems in judgment, analysis and reasoning. Their day to day life gets adversely affected and they become dependent on a significant other for almost all activities outside their home, as they may be unable to find their way back alone. Studies have indicated that bees exposed to neonics showed a similar loss in memory, judgment, and their ability to navigate home. This is the primary reason that rendered them incapable of returning to their hives and eventually becoming extinct as a species. If dementia is increasing in numbers, it may be directly related to the planting and consumption of GMO foods loaded with neonics. Not only dementia, all major diseases including Parkinson's and cancer are continuously rising at a staggering pace.

A recent study done in England tracked the use of neonics for over a 10 year period, and found direct evidence between this insecticide and bee colony losses. This was the largest study conducted with actual field trials, which has confirmed without any reasonable doubt the intense harm neonics are inflicting on our food chain supply and the environment. The U.S. Geological Survey has also published a report indicating neonics being found in half of the streams they examined. The study confirms that these insectcides are easily transported from soil to water, thus making them highly toxic to organisms which form the food base for fish and birds who eat acquatic insects.

If all this evidence was not enough, experiments conducted on various animals that were fed GMO diets have revealed some shocking fertility issues. According to Russian biologist Alexey V. Surov, the third generation of hamsters who were fed GMO soy for two years became totally infertile, that is, they lost their ability to have babies. While Austrian researchers reported that the fourth generation of mice on GMO corn became completely infertile. Many USA farmers using GMO feeds have reported infertile pigs and cows. If the bees have died due to neonics and animals are becoming infertile, what would be the fate of the human race with GMO corn, soy, and other genetically modified crops? This is the most important question that needs to be addressed before the elected leaders, members of parliament and other officials of any nation ever think of passing any bill to introduce such crops.

It took a great collective effort of over 40 years by the people of USA, Europe and other parts of the world, to wake up their governments and concerned authorities to ban PCB's made by the same Monsanto. It was only after chemical traces were found across the USA in fish, oysters, shrimp, bald eagles, and milk, when EPA and the World Health Organization were forced to declare them cancerous, which resulted into their ultimate worldwide ban. Now with the GMO crops and foods the harm is even greater than the PCB's. Not only traces of neonics that have been found in fish and other water based animals, but the issues of infertility and the gigantic increase in major diseases would clearly mark the end of times for the human race on earth. There won't be any World War III, as predicted by many, to unleash nuclear weapons and bombs to destroy us. The GMO crops and foods will become the ultimate nuclear tools to eliminate all life forms from earth, and we as a race will be responsible for our own doom.

This book only provides a brief history of Monsanto and GMO's, and if you wish to know more, I would recommend you read 'Seeds of Deception' by Jeffrey M. Smith, and 'Altered Genes, Twisted Truth' by Steven M. Druker. In this journey of going back to nature and healing yourself, it was important to make you aware about GMO foods and the great harm they have inflicted, and continue to do so, and the catastrophe that awaits if no action is taken to halt their introduction into third world countries. The need to stop GMO seeds from taking over our food chain and supplies has never been greater than today, and there's something each one of us can do. Every single action, big or small, will add up collectively to help in sustaining our natural practices of agriculture to reap the harvests of pure healthy foods. There is no other way, but to get involved and take responsibility of your body and all that goes inside it.

Coming back to the subject of eating raw vegetables and fruits, which will serve as the building blocks to regenerate all your internal organs, it is essential you look for organic and non-GMO produce. If you live in the USA or Europe you will easily find a huge variety available. In India many small scale farmers have begun growing organic produce, but you'll have to make an effort to look for the right products by doing a background check or visiting the related farms. While in countries like Ghana, farming methods are by far organic till now, but you should verify the source and do the required research to make sure you're getting what you want.

You can even grow some vegetables in your own backyard, or go a step forward by making a small investment to begin your own organic farming, which could turn into an extremely rewarding business. In Switzerland, most people grow their own vegetables in their backyard. They consult and plan with the neighbors what each will grow to have a greater variety, and then exchange or barter their produce with each other. If the Swiss can do it, why not you? The world needs a whole lot of organic farmers and there is enough farmland in every country, but not enough people to venture into this noble and profitable cause. Once you have some in-house practical experience, it can easily lead to farming on a larger scale.

Weekly fasts will be the first step for entering into a new way of life and beginning the process to rejuvenate the body, cells, and all organs. The second step would be to introduce raw organic vegetables and fruits into your daily meals, as they are the essential raw materials to rebuild every cell and organ. It is important that you have a good serving of raw vegetables with your morning and evening meals. If you have a problem having them in raw form, you can place them in a pan and lightly sauté for 3 to 4 minutes. Don't forget to add fresh fruits to your morning meal to get fully energized for the day's work and activities, and follow the two meals a day regimen.

The third step on the path of this highway of a new way of life is to begin having a revolutionary health drink – a drink that has been known to mankind from thousands of years, but forgotten in these modern times. Since time immemorial people have consumed a miraculous concoction of Apple cider vinegar, ginger, cinnamon, and honey to heal, cleanse, detoxify, and super-charge the human body with strength and vigor. In 2003, I met an 82 year old lady in Washington D.C., who looked as if she was in her sixties. Her name was Vivian Haswell, a celebrated poet, and she shared with me the following story about her life and health.

"Back in the eighties I was stricken with heart failure. I was in the hospital more in than out. I was devastated, for I was in real estate, operating a group home for boys, and I needed strength and health. A friend of my husband brought me a little paperback book which was the published journal of a Doctor back in the 1800's. The book was very conclusive of the benefits of vinegar, honey, and ginger to our health. According to his journal, he could cure anything with these ingredients. Time after time he had recorded true cases of what happened when he persuaded his patients to begin having these natural health boosters. I thought, why not? I was prone to die with this ailment, and according to his journal, the heart had been one of the organs that highly benefitted from this concoction. I also remembered back when I was a child in New York, in the hayfields the men were drinking a combination of these items; apple cider vinegar, honey, ginger, cinnamon. I began to mix a gallon, set it in the refrigerator, and every time I was thirsty, I drank this concoction. It took three months for me to notice a difference, and it was a marked one. I felt more alive, the frequency of visits to the hospital significantly decreased. Petty issues which earlier would perturb me ceased to affect me; bowel problems, headaches, anxiety, restlessness and other physiological and psychological symptoms of stress that I had decreased slowly and steadily. I shared the secret with others but they laughed it off, but I persisted as I saw the difference in myself.

In 1995, I was stricken with a stroke. It was terrible, I was dressed to go swimming, when suddenly I felt a hammer hit me, and it touched everything from head to toe. I was in my bathing suit, I was 75, and was scared when I discovered I could not talk. Gradually the stroke ceased and recovery was rapid. I was a halleluiah person gone ape when I walked without pain, or problem, I had no handicap, I was ok. I figured somehow, the vinegar, honey, ginger drink had been a stopper against this malady. I was healed, and I continued with the drink. Apples keep the doctor away, while Honey is a 'perfect' food, according to this Doctor's report; it cures all ills. The guards gave Jesus vinegar, why? It would give him strength to endure a little longer and suffer more. He refused it, knowing this. I never drink any pops and seldom drink coffee. I drink my concoction and laugh at those who tease me. I am a very healthy woman of 82, and often thought to be in my sixties. My skin is smooth, hair is healthy, and mind is sharp."

What a true and great testimony from an 82 year old young lady on the amazing effects of this wonderful concoction of apple cider vinegar, ginger, cinnamon, and honey. Before going any further, it would be worthwhile to indulge in a brief study and analyze the individual benefits of each of these natural products that are available everywhere, and determine their historical relevance and healing properties.

Apple cider vinegar: This vinegar has a long history of curing numerous health issues and has been in use since ages. Hippocrates – the father of medicine prescribed this tonic in 400 B.C. to his patients to heal every disease, and maintain good health and vigor. In ancient Greece, Rome, and Egypt, it was widely used as a healing elixir, or a cure-all remedy as far back as 3000 B.C. The soldiers of Julius Caesar used this tonic to stay healthy and free from disease, while Christopher Columbus on his way to discover America had barrels of vinegar on his vessel. The Chinese and Japanese have long used it as a foremost healing and prevention tonic to ward off disease and ill-health.

You may have heard it often – An apple a day keeps the doctor away, as it contains a whole lot of nutrients that are good for you to be in peak health. But in the present times the kind of apples that are available will rather take you to the doctor, as they're loaded with harmful pesticides. The common clear vinegar available in the supermarkets is made from such apples and also passes through a distillation process that removes most of the healing properties. This is not the vinegar you should look for. The right type of vinegar is made from crushed organic apples, which are then matured in wooden barrels to increase the natural effects of fermentation. It is brown in color, and you will find cobweb like particles at the bottom of the bottle which are known as the mother enzymes and contain enormous healing properties.

Regular use of the vinegar alone results in multiple health benefits that are backed by actual testimonials and case histories of numerous bona fide users. There is substantial evidence of its enormous benefits presented in the book, 'Apple Cider Vinegar Miracle Health System' by Paul and Patricia Bragg. They call it – Nature's Healing Miracle, and explain how it detoxifies the bloodstream and various organs of the body, promoting healthy blood flow to the heart, brain and the entire body. Toxins in the body are the main cause behind every health issue, whether major or minor, and apple cider vinegar provides the force to eliminate them. No toxins – no disease, that is the simplest law of nature. Pectin, a soluble fiber in vinegar assists to dilute cancer causing dietary fats from the colon. It also contains a natural chemical that helps to make the heart stronger, remove artery plaque, normalize high blood pressure and eliminate LDL (bad) cholesterol, which greatly reduces the risk of heart attacks and strokes. Among many other benefits, it helps to improve blood sugar levels, lose weight, improve digestion, heal constipation, fight kidney problems, relieve headaches, and keep your joints youthful by flushing out the acid crystals responsible for premature ageing. You must get a copy of this book to know more about the Miracle Health System introduced by Paul Bragg, and his legacy of good health now being carried on by his daughter, Patricia Bragg.

I have personally experienced the amazing benefits through regular use and the feedback received from my numerous customers who are using this product. From the various brands available in the market, the one I find to be the ultimate is Bragg Apple cider vinegar, as it is organic, raw, unfiltered, unpasteurized, and with the Mother – the cobweb like substances that contain enzymes and minerals, which you'll not find in regular vinegars. It is easily available in the USA at a reasonable price, but in places like India the price is almost four times higher. Looking at its tremendous healing benefits I began shipping this to Ghana, which is my second home. It is available there at various IPMC locations at a price only marginally higher than in the USA, which is due to the freight and custom duty factor. My goal is not to profit, but to facilitate natural healing in people who are suffering from various ailments, and also to promote good health in the population at large. Whenever I am in Ghana, I usually come across customers who share their healing stories with me, and in a nutshell, below is a minor list of the benefits they have experienced with Apple cider vinegar:

Visits to the hospital or a doctor greatly reduced.

No cough or cold for over 2 years.

Asthma completely healed.

High blood pressure that existed from years, became normal.

Diabetes came under control and blood sugar levels became normal.

Experienced substantial weight loss.

Bad cholesterol LDL came down to normal.

Migraines and headaches completely disappeared.

Helped improve Arthritis and severe joint pains, and walking became pain-free.

Improved digestion and completely healed constipation that existed from years.

Greatly increased energy levels.

Leg-cramps totally gone.

Cinnamon: This delicious spice comes from the inner bark of a tree known as Cinnamomum, and has been known for its medicinal properties from thousands of years, dating as far back as ancient Egypt. In the olden days it was regarded as an exclusive herb for the rich and elite due to its unique healing nature and limited availability. Today, it is widely available and modern medicine has acknowledged its healing properties by conducting a significant amount of scientific research, which has confirmed its amazing health benefits.

Cinnamon is full of antioxidants that provide protection to the human body from the damage caused by free radicals. It has anti-inflammatory properties that help to fight infections and repair tissue damage. With regular use it has shown to reduce high blood pressure, LDL (bad) cholesterol, risk of heart disease, and increase HDL (good) cholesterol. It helps to lower blood sugar levels and greatly aids people suffering from diabetes by decreasing the amount of glucose that enters the blood after meals. A number of clinical trials have suggested that a daily dose of 1-5 grams of cinnamon can lower the amount of fasting blood sugar to almost normal levels. The healing effects of cinnamon have also been noted on people suffering from dementia, Parkinson's and Alzheimer's disease. In animal studies, it has shown to reduce the growth of cancer cells and tumors, while a study conducted on HIV patients showed that cinnamon is beneficial and an effective treatment course.

Ginger: This is one of the most powerful spices as it contains a variety of vitamins and minerals, and is loaded with a number of medicinal properties. It is a common ingredient in Indian and Asian cuisine and has been used from thousands of years for medicinal purposes. It has been well-known to relieve digestive problems, obesity, diabetes, heart disease, muscle pain and soreness. It contains tremendous anti-inflammatory properties that greatly help in reducing joint and knee pain. A study published in the Cancer Prevention Research Journal indicated that ginger reduced inflammation markers in the colon within a month, which means, it may greatly decrease the risk of colon cancer. Many other studies have also proven that it lowers blood sugar levels, which strongly suggest, it has anti-diabetic benefits. It has also shown in clinical trials to reduce LDL (bad) cholesterol that would ultimately lower the risk of heart disease.

Honey: This wonderful natural sweetener has been around from over 4,000 years, and was the main source to sweeten any food before sugar came into existence. Besides the sweet part, honey contains amazing antiseptic, antioxidant, and cleansing properties that made it an integral part of natural medicines and treatments to heal cuts, cure various ailments and diseases, fight infection, reduce inflammation, and aid in tissue healing. It is well-known and used since ages to effectively treat digestive disorders, diarrhea, stomach ulcers, gastroenteritis, improve skin condition and boost memory. Today it is the focus of a great deal of scientific research by the modern medical establishment. It is widely used in cough mixtures as it has a soothing effect and greatly aids in the healing process. In addition, tests have confirmed that honey contains a wide range of vitamins and minerals, which makes it a great replacement for sugar to provide real nutrients to your body. It is considered as a transporter of the healing properties of herbs and spices to the cells and organs of the body. So any time honey is added, it enhances the medicinal benefits of the formulation to provide healing to the body in a much more powerful manner.

This amazing concoction of Apple cider vinegar, cinnamon, ginger, and honey will provide healing to your body in a variety of ways. The individual benefits of each have been highlighted in detail – all you need is to conduct a trial and see the results for yourself. To make it easier, you can begin with the vinegar and honey alone, which is simple to prepare. In a glass of lukewarm water add one teaspoon each of vinegar and honey, stir well and sip slowly to enjoy the great taste. The best time to have this is an hour before breakfast or an hour after dinner. There is no need to overdo it, one glass would be more than enough for you to gradually experience the healing and changes it brings. Rome wasn't built in a day, nor will your body heal overnight as it is all a gradual process. Once the benefits of vinegar and honey become clearly visible, you can then add a little cinnamon powder and note how that helps. The same process should be followed with ginger.

If you are diabetic, it would be good to experiment initially with half a teaspoon of honey and see the effects on your blood sugar levels. If you ask your doctor about this, the answer could be a no, but clinical studies have proven that honey is a healthier choice in a diabetic diet compared to sugar and other sweeteners, such as splenda, aspartame, or saccharin. In his book, 'The Honey Revolution', Dr. Ron Fessenden explains that in a glucose intolerant person, blood sugar response after honey intake is much lower than when compared with blood sugar response after having sugar. It would be worthwhile to get a copy of this book and find out how honey is able to perform this remarkable feat and its various other health benefits. Unless you do not get the required information and facts about honey, and then experiment to see how your body responds, you'll not get any definite answers.

The fourth step into this new way of life is to set up a regular daily routine to take care of your body. This should primarily include water intake of 1.5 to 2 liters and a good exercise regimen. It is important to keep your body hydrated and not allow the blood to become thicker, which places undue stress on all the organs. Every day the human body loses about 2 liters of water through perspiration and elimination. It is important to replace that loss to keep the blood at the required density level. Otherwise, the heart has to work harder to pump blood and transport nutrients, which weakens it to a great extent, and that in turn is detrimental to every other organ in the body. A daily exercise program is essential for a healthy fruitful body, and this should include – cardio, strength training, yoga, breathing exercises, and Reiki. My previous book, 'Mental, Physical and Spiritual Health' can help you organize these important elements of your daily life to attain physical, mental, and spiritual well-being.

The fifth step, which is of utmost importance, is to make a resolution to love your 'Self' and understand the true meaning of it. This should not be like a New Year's resolution, which many folks make every year, that lasts only for a couple of weeks. Then, they wait for the following year to make another one, and this continues endlessly without a single resolution turning fruitful. You need to understand that every day when you wake up in the morning alive and breathing, it is a new day, a new year. If yesterday you missed implementing the resolution to love your 'Self', you can do it today. Not only is it important to understand this concept, it is an important requirement to begin this new way of life.

Most people believe these words are the gospel truth, when they tell their spouse, parents or children – I love you. The truth is, you cannot love anyone else if you don't love your Self. For example – if you love them, wouldn't you do all that is required to keep them happy? If they're not feeling well or have some serious health issues, wouldn't you be concerned and take immediate steps to help get their health in order? Why would you do all that? Because, you truly love them. But do you really? If you have answered yes, wouldn't you wish to stand tall and be there for them as long they're physically alive on Earth, or would you like to be a burden upon them? Imagine, some drastic health issue strikes you, for instance a heart attack, stroke, paralysis, kidney failure, or the worst of all, cancer. What would happen to your love then? Would you be then able to take care of them, or will they have to take care of you?

Understanding this new way of life and making practical applications of these five steps to give the utmost importance to the body you live in, is the only way to light that candle of self-love. The five steps should become a part of you as a deeply ingrained habit. Any acts you do repeatedly for a month help you to become pregnant with them. As you continue with the repetition, the pregnancy becomes deep-rooted in three months, and finally after nine months you are born into that new way of life. According to ancient wisdom these words hold great meaning and significance in our lives: "As I do, so I become. Every single action that I perform gets recorded in me. These imprints become habits and ultimately mold my character and destiny."

As you move toward the final chapter of this journey to go back to Nature and heal your Self, the only question I need to ask you at this point is: Do you believe you are the master of your destiny or an insignificant bystander having no control over your life? If you believe you're the master, then there is no obstacle that you cannot overcome to follow these five steps and ignite the candle of self-love, to lighten up your life with good health, and to experience real heaven in this Garden of Eden that we call planet Earth. Self-mastery is the highest degree anyone can possibly attain to achieve material and spiritual success in every single area of your life, and it all begins from self-love and the true realization of who you really are.

Chapter 7

How to Heal your Self

A beautiful story that I read on the internet reflects the reality of who we truly are. Once an eagle's egg was placed in the nest of a chicken. When the egg hatched and the little eagle grew up with other chickens, it always thought of itself to be a chicken. So the eagle did what the chickens did, and scratched in the dirt for seeds and flew no more than a few feet. One day he saw an eagle flying high up in the open skies and was greatly impressed at how effortlessly the majestic bird was cruising in the air. He wondered what an outstanding bird this must be, and lamented at the thought of being merely a little chicken who couldn't fly more than a few feet. He imagined how different and exciting life would have been if he had been like that bird, soaring high above to explore the great blue skies. Not realizing that he was also an eagle, he lived the life of a chicken with limitations, and eventually died as a chicken without spreading his wings and gliding high up in the skies.

There exists a great comparison between the eagle's story and our reality. When we are born as a human being, and as we grow up in the company of other humans, we do what most people do and live an ordinary existence like the majority. When we see some eagles (successful people) rising high above others, we are greatly impressed with their achievements and believe they're the lucky or chosen ones, while we are born to struggle and suffer like the masses. Not realizing that we too have the seed to become successful, we live the life of an ordinary human being with limitations, and eventually die as an ordinary person without exploring our talents and soaring high up in life.

If you will think of yourself as only a human being, that would be equivalent to the eagle thinking of itself to be a chicken. The truth is, you are the Spirit inside this human body with the power to rise and soar as high you may possibly envision. There are no limitations on you, except those that are self-imposed. The biggest limitation which the majority impose upon themselves is the state and condition of the body they live in. If the organs inside you function in a limitless and optimum manner as they are programmed to, only then, can you too function in a similar manner. If the organs are not working right, it could very well mean that the body is corrupted with wrong elements. Then, only corrupt or wrong actions can happen through such a body.

From thousands of years corruption has been an integral part of human nature. It has become like a plague or virus that has penetrated every segment of our behavior and societies. Have you ever wondered why? In various scriptures, flesh has been referred to as evil, weak, or corrupt. Anything that becomes corrupted will emit corrupt vibrations, which will eventually corrupt and weaken the system it controls. You don't need to know any rocket science to understand this simple theory. If the vehicle through which we operate, the human body, is corrupted, it is obvious that all the organs, cells, and flesh, which are part of it, will become corrupted too. The only way to rid the flesh of such impurities, is to rid the body from all corrupted forces.

Corruption in the world today is generally defined in various ways, which include: stealing, embezzlement, fraud, bribery, and a most modern and dignified word – lobbying. Each of these acts are corrupt in nature and are generally related to the misuse of public authority by politicians and people holding positions of power. When you vote people into offices to run the affairs of your city or nation, the biggest complain we have is that most officials become corrupt. Then, they perform corrupt actions to gain personal benefits or favor a certain elite segment of the community at the expense of the common man. When companies like Monsanto and its partners spend over USD 30 million to lobby members of the US House of Representatives to pass a bill like the DARK Act, and take over the basic rights to know what's in the foods of those very voters who voted them into office, that becomes the most elite form of corruption in the so-called civilized society.

In sports bodies and organizations, which do not directly affect the common man, corruption has been gradually on the rise in the 21st century. In 2015, the FIFA corruption scandal rocked the football world, when the United States Federal

Bureau of Investigation indicted 14 top officials including a former president of the federation on charges of receiving USD 150 million in bribes. In India, BCCI, the governing body that controls and runs the affairs of the most popular sport in Asia, cricket, have had numerous scandals involving bribery and money laundering, in which top officials and even players have been involved. When investigations are launched by the governing bodies, the corrupt acts only increase, as the officials of the investigative bodies become a part of the corrupt nexus.

When a political party or any leader comes to power through a democratic process in any nation, it means, that they were able to influence people to vote in their favor. This is usually done against a backdrop of a wide range of campaign promises. Today, in all developing countries the subject of corruption is one of the most significant issues in an election year, as people are fed up with political unethicalness. During the campaign trail it is common for the leaders of the opposition parties to highlight the corruption scandals of the government in power. They will normally use popular campaign slogans, such as, "If elected, we will uproot corruption and not tolerate dishonesty from even a single member of our government." Many elections are won in a landslide manner on such anti-corruption platforms, but soon the new government ministers and officials stand accused of similar acts.

The story is no different in every nation where the democratic process is being followed. After elections the political parties or leaders may change, but the actual acts of corruption witness little or no change. This is how it has been going on, and it will continue in the same manner as long as the flesh is weak, evil, or corrupt. Corruption in government, religious, sports bodies and everyday life will not go away, unless we understand the root cause behind it and make efforts to correct the basic malfunction in the human body, of which the flesh is an integral part. In actual reality, it is not the flesh, but rather the body itself that is weak or corrupt.

The condition of our bodies is the sole reason for the corruption that exists in every nation. It may be easy to blame the leaders, elected officials and governments, but very difficult to accept that each of us are an integral part of the vicious circle responsible to create and sustain corruption. While we expect the elected officials not to be corrupt and do what is right for the country, very often, our contribution is minimal. Most people will do whatever it takes to avoid taxes, custom duties, and other essential roles of being a good citizen. Many individuals involved in small trade will not even register their businesses and completely evade payment of taxes. While a number of individuals and corporations around the world find ways to avoid the legitimate taxes that are due to the revenue department.

In developing nations where the government runs essential amenities like water and electricity, it is common to see people misuse them and avoid payment by way of illegal connections, or meter tampering. It is the same fellows who would complain the loudest if water or electricity shortage hits their nation. They would hold the government and elected officials responsible for their inability to provide these basic amenities. We should never forget that we all are a part of the big circle of life on Earth. Our government is not made up of foreigners, but our own citizens, and it is we who vote them into office. According to true democratic principles, it is truly meant to be a government of the people, for the people, and by the people.

It is important to understand that we are all actively involved in helping corruption thrive, circulate and percolate at full force. Where our personal relations are concerned, the majority of us are deeply entrenched in corrupt activities. The most intimate relationship on Earth is of man and woman, and through the institute of marriage it lays the foundation for our existence. If we apply the true democratic principles to this relationship, it should mean a marriage of the two, for the two, and by the two individuals. But it is rare to find a couple that apply these principles and live in love and harmony. Not only should both partners be faithful, the element of trust, respect, and love should be an integral part of this most valuable and treasured relationship. Scriptures reiterate that one should stay faithful and not commit adultery, but you openly see married partners doing the opposite. Imagine, children born and raised from such corrupted marriages, what kind of adults will they turn into? Have you ever given any serious thought to this major element of child up-bringing and the values we impart through such corrupted relationships?

The basic mindset of the majority of people in the world today has been crafted by such unhealthy relationships, and the sole reason is the state of our corrupted bodies. Instead of complaining that others are not doing their work honestly, we should rather focus that time and energy on ourselves to take care of the bodies we live in. Change always begins from one point of a circle, and that point is you. Nobody has the power to change others, as that is the sole prerogative of every individual. When one person begins the process to change and enter a circle, he would automatically touch and impact all others in that circle. Such a circle will not remain corrupted any longer, rather it will become a revolutionary circle of love and change.

The journey of change cannot begin till you realize your true identity, as to who you really are and where exactly you reside inside the human body. The main engine of the body is the heart, and it is also the home of the Spirit. If the heart stops beating, the Spirit cannot live there any longer, and the moment it leaves – all other organs shut down and the body is declared dead. A great many books of wisdom point this out clearly with words like: For where your treasure is, there will your heart be also, or your heart is where your treasure is. From the heart flows love – the creative energy of the Spirit and the universe. It is love that forms the heart and then flows from it endlessly to the rest of the body. Can there be any greater treasure than love – the force of all creation in the Universe?

Since thousands of years we all have been searching to find treasures in the outside world to become successful and wealthy, and not realizing that the 'Spirit' inside the human body contains the greatest treasure of all – the power of love and creation. How will you find what you search in the world outside when what you seek is right here, within your heart. You are the Spirit inside a human body and there is no end to you. There was never a time you were not, and there will never be a time you will not be. The power of love is your legacy and you are an eternal part of the soul of the world, and all the hidden treasures of the universe are inside you.

Paulo Coelho, in his best-selling book, 'The Alchemist', describes this phenomenon with a remarkable tale of a shepherd in Spain, who while resting near an abandoned church dreams of a hidden treasure at the pyramids in Egypt. To pursue the dream, he sells his sheep and begins the journey towards the magical land. On the way he's robbed, and has to work for almost a year at a crystal shop to continue with the expedition. Finally, when he arrives at the destination and begins to dig for the treasure, a group of refugees almost beat him to death. When he tells them about his dream, the leader of the group laughs and exclaims that he too had a dream about a hidden treasure beneath the roots of a sycamore in an abandoned church in Spain, but he was not stupid to go all the way to a far off land, just because of a dream. At that point of time the shepherd realizes that the hidden treasure he saw in the dream was in the church itself, the place where he rested with his sheep. So he heads back to Spain and finds the treasure right beneath the roots of the sycamore, a treasure he travelled far and wide to search for, and endured enormous hardships on the way.

This magical tale illustrates the true identity and location of the treasure we all seek, which only a select few are able to find. Although every single person dreams to be well off financially, the enormous gap between success and failure continues to widen. The reasons may not be hard to find. As long you look for success externally in a far-off place, or believe in becoming rich overnight by stumbling to some hidden treasure or through unfair means, you'll be on the wrong path of life burdened with unnecessary hardships. Your treasure is indeed where your heart is. This is not somewhere outside but within you, and is the true source of all love and creation responsible to move the universe forward. Not only do you have the power to dream, you are also truly gifted with the creative forces of love to create a life according to those dreams.

Dreams originate from two places, one from the Mind and the other from the Heart. It is the mind that dreams when we sleep at night, and one such dream led the shepherd to the pyramids. On the way he found elements of struggle, deceit, and pain, but no hidden treasure in the end. After being badly beaten and bruised by the refugees, when he finally stood up and looked at the pyramids, it was his heart that realized where the treasure was. This story is laden with mysteries, but eventually points toward an eternal truth. When you dream from the mind, the path to realization will be full of struggle, pain, deceit, and failure in the end. Whereas, if the dream originates from the heart, success is guaranteed with minimal effort as all the spiritual forces of the universe come forward to assist you. Why? Because, you – the Spirit, is a part of them and your dream becomes their dream.

Since ages there has been a war raging inside each of us, a war between the Mind and the Heart, or Bad and Good, or as some people term it, Devil and God. It is the Mind where anger, greed, deceit, and corruption flourish, while the Heart simply pours out love and affection. Mind is selfish and only knows how to take, and will go to any extent to utilize the forces of deceit and greed to get what it wants. On the other hand, the Heart is selfless and only knows how to give, and will also go to any extent to utilize the forces of love to give to others abundantly. When we refer to the Heart, it is actually a direct reference to the Spirit, which is the true source of the love that flows from it.

Neglect and a lack of care for the bodies we live in greatly helps the Mind to take control and become dominant. The unhealthy foods and drinks, dangerous drugs and medications that are constantly taken without giving any second thoughts, greatly assist the negative and corrupt forces in the mind to multiply and grow like cancer. While the heart gets weaker when the body is neglected, the Spirit becomes a helpless prisoner, chained in an unhealthy body and compelled to view this human neglect through its prison bars. A weaker body benefits the Mind in every way to continue its reign over the Spirit.

It will be of great help if you realize that the Mind is simply a tool provided to the Spirit for various activities. Just like a tennis racquet is only a tool to play tennis, and when you master the way to use it effectively, you become a good player. A tennis racquet becomes a powerful tool in the hands of a well-trained professional and can pave the way to win championships, and a whole lot admiration, money and fame. In a similar manner, a Mind becomes a powerful tool in the hands of a person who has mastered its use. As a matter of fact, the Mind is an extremely obedient and powerful servant, but an obnoxious and dangerous master. An ancient Sage once remarked, "The One who wins over the mind, wins the entire Universe."

People often talk about Resurrection and the need to be Born Again, which does not happen by frequenting any religious abode. This state rather manifests from the love that is allowed to flow freely from the heart. The Spirit caged in an unhealthy, sick, or diseased body is crying for resurrection and to be born again every single day. It does not want to be a helpless prisoner at the mercy of the dominant mind, while the body continues to degenerate. Every Spirit is an eternal part of the divine force we call God or Nature, and is capable of magical feats to transform our world consumed by hatred, greed, corruption, terrorism, and needless wars. We all are divine beings held together by a single common thread of love. The only way we can express our true divinity is to allow the free flow of the energy of love from the heart. And that can only happen – when our body is healthy and free from sickness, disease, drugs and medications.

To become a champion in any sport, the three most essential factors are: A healthy body, a healthy diet, and regular practice. The more you practice, the better you'll be in any given sport or profession. But to be able to do that and put in those long hours to attain mastery and become a champion, a healthy body and a healthy diet is foremost. If that part is missing, the practice sessions cannot last long enough to give you the required skills to win matches or competitions. You can look at the top athletes and champions of the world sports and see what kind of athletic physiques they possess. It is not as if they were gifted or born with such phenomenal physiques, it is by way of sheer hard work and a steadfast dedication toward the achievement of their dreams. Needless to say, without a healthy diet it is impossible to have such wonderful physiques. True champions understand these basic truths, get down to the required hard work and lead a disciplined well-planned life. It is no wonder – the top tennis, basketball, and soccer players not only inspire millions of people, but also earn millions every year.

Our journey on Earth is the greatest sport of all, and to become a champion of life the three most essential factors are no different than any other sport. A healthy body, a healthy diet, and regular practice of the unique talent we individually possess are the ingredients required to attain self-mastery and become successful in our lives and professions. The importance of the human body cannot be underscored, and there is an ancient Sufi tale that beautifully exemplifies its real value in an amazing manner.

Once there was a fellow named John who was deeply intrigued about the real value of the human body. He felt this was one of the most important assets of an earthly life, but was confused as to why the majority of people ignored and abused it to the maximum. So he went to a very learned teacher and asked him if he could tell him the real value of the human body. The teacher took out a glittering stone from his pocket and handed over to him, with instructions that he should go to the three nearby cities and find out from three different tradesmen the value of this stone, and then return back.

As John entered the first city, he met a trader selling fruits and vegetables. As he showed him the glittering stone and asked what he thought would be the value, the trader looked at it with deep intent, and after careful thought offered a bag of fruits and vegetables for it. John had instructions not to sell or part with it, only to find out the value and return the stone back to the teacher.

Moving forward John proceeded to the next city, and this time decided to look for an ornament trader who might be a better judge to determine the real value. As he took out the glittering piece of stone from his pocket, the trader was simply astonished as he had never seen such a unique master-piece in his entire life. He offered him a million dollars, and when John said it was not for sale, the trader counter-offered two, then three, and eventually five million dollars to buy it.

Leaving behind the ornament trader in a desperate situation John proceeded to the next city, and decided to look for a diamond trader as he was now even more perplexed about what the real value of this glittering stone might be. Unlike the ornament trader, the diamond trader placed no value on the stone, nor did he make any effort to buy it. He told John that the stone was simply priceless and no amount of wealth in the entire world would be sufficient to buy it.

John returned back to the teacher and narrated the ordeal he went through to find out the value of the glittering stone. After listening carefully to his story, the learned teacher said: "If this piece of stone was considered priceless by the diamond trader, worth five million by the ornament trader, and equal to a bag of fruits and vegetables by the fruit trader, then what do you think would be the value of the human body, which is equipped with various organs and senses that truly are the most amazing wonders of the universe. What possible price would you figure out for a pair of eyes that make you see the beauty all around, or a pair of legs that move you from place to place, or the sense of touch, taste, or sound? And what amount will you pay for the amazing heart and mind that the human body is equipped with?"

The truth is, the real value of the human body is indeed priceless. If you had that glittering stone the learned teacher gave John, the level of care for the stone will be in direct comparison to the value you place on it. Likewise, if you consider the value of the Human Body to be equal to a bag of fruits and vegetables, you'll care for it accordingly. If you consider it to be worth five million dollars, you'll definitely care and protect it with a little more attention. And if you realize the value of the human body is indeed priceless, the care and protection will be in accordance with that value. It all depends whether you are like the vegetable and fruit trader, the ornament trader, or the diamond trader.

The truth is considered bitter, and the bitter truth I must tell you is that majority of us are like the fruit and vegetable trader, as we hardly place any value on the human body and abuse it to the maximum with wrong foods, an unhealthy lifestyle, dangerous drugs and medications, and a whole lot of other harmful things. There are only a few who are like the ornament trader, and an even smaller fraction like the diamond trader, who know the real value and take care of the human body in accordance with its priceless stature.

Although highlighted earlier in great detail, I would like to re-emphasize these facts to help you understand the most significant truths of life. Without any doubt the greatest wonder machine on Earth is the human body. It contains amazing instruments known as organs, which no science can replicate. Every organ is not only self-healing, but also keeps on replenishing itself indefinitely. As you're the owner and inhabitant of this wonder machine, your only responsibility is to ensure the self-healing and rejuvenating process goes on in the most efficient manner. You are indeed the creator of your body and whatever condition it is in presently, it's your very own creation. You do possess the prerequisite powers to re-create your body and organs any time you wish to, by simply changing your lifestyle.

The human body has over 37 trillion cells responsible for various functions, including healing and regeneration. Every three months, on average, old cells die and new ones take birth. Ancient healing sciences have long stood by time-tested principles of how the human body degenerates and regenerates by the kind of lifestyle an individual has. They all confirm one basic truth – Health and regeneration is the natural state of the body, while disease and degeneration is its unnatural state. Depending upon regular physical activity and proper diet, one can stay young and vibrant in every sphere of their lives even at age one hundred. Individuals like Thomas Parr have clearly demonstrated this truth with a healthy lifespan of 152 years.

Even modern medical science has now published facts about how long it takes a human body to regenerate and develop new organs, skin, and cells. They explain that regeneration takes place in two basic steps. First, the old cell matter is channeled to the intestines through the blood stream for elimination with the food waste. Second, new cell matter is created from nutrients found in foods that an individual consumes. These nutrients are absorbed through the intestinal walls into the blood stream and then distributed to the entire body for the regeneration process to continue constantly. According to their research, new red blood cells are formed every 120 days, new skeleton every 90 days, new brain cells and tissue every 60 days, new stomach lining every 5 days, and a new liver every 45 days.

If you now understand how the human body functions, it doesn't matter in what state your body and the various organs are at the present moment. Nor does it matter how badly you may have abused the body with wrong foods, drugs and medications. The good news is, the moment you begin to feed the same body with healthy foods, the regeneration process begins to move in the right direction from the nutrients derived from those foods. Change never happens overnight as it is a gradual step by step process, so it is important to realize how this works and then start working constructively towards that change.

Our lives on Earth are governed by universal laws, and one vital law is the law of sow and reap. This law is applicable to every area of our life, including regeneration and degeneration of the body. Since new cell matter and the subsequent organ development take place according to nutrients from foods, it's all contingent on what kind of foods you consume. Good foods will obviously provide good nutrients, resulting into good cell matter and healthy organs. On the other hand, unhealthy foods will undoubtedly provide unfit nutrients, resulting into bad cell matter and weak organs. The law of sow and reap plays out perfectly in every segment of our lives. As we are the creators of our body, the creation will happen exactly in accordance with the foods and nutrients we provide our bodies every day. Of course, regular physical exercise and yoga have their own benefits in keeping the body fit, but there is definitely no substitute to foods in the regeneration and degeneration processes of the body.

As you begin your journey to transform yourself, and in case you have any major health issues and are on prescription drugs to keep them under check, it is important to work hand in hand with your doctor or health care provider. It is also important to select your doctor with care – the one who understands that the modern health care system is in fact a disease-care system. It only cares for the disease and keeps it under control with drugs, but does not provide any healing. As long as you continue the intake of prescribed drugs for a certain ailment, it will contain that problem without actually healing it, while causing intense harm to other organs and create brand new ailments at the same time. It would be worthwhile to discuss with your doctor about the true meaning of the Hippocratic Oath he or she took upon graduating from medical college.

Hippocrates was a Greek physician who practiced medicine in 400 BC. He is widely known as the Father of Western Medicine in recognition of his contributions as the founder of the Hippocratic School of Medicine. He greatly believed in the natural healing force inside the body and was never in favor of prescribing drugs, or administering any specialized treatment. For every acute problem, he prescribed fasting and a regular intake of apple cider vinegar. He strongly advocated, that to eat when you are sick is to feed your sickness. The original Hippocratic Oath that doctors had to take upon graduating, stipulated: "With regard to healing the sick, I will devise and order for them the best diet, and

I will take care they suffer no hurt or damage." While the modern oath has been modified and highlights: "If I am to care adequately for the sick, I will prevent disease whenever I can, for prevention is preferable to cure."

Thomas A. Edison, the great American genius who invented the light bulb, motion picture camera, phonograph, and developed the system of electric power generation to homes and businesses, rendered this eye-opening statement on doctors and medicine – "The doctor of the future will give no medicine, but will interest his patients in the care of the human frame, in a proper diet, and in the cause and prevention of disease."

If you notice carefully, there is no difference between the words of Thomas A. Edison and the Hippocratic Oath. Both talk about the best or proper diet and how to care for the human body to prevent disease, as prevention is preferable to cure. You need to have an in-depth conversation with your doctor about the true meaning and proper understanding of this Oath. The majority of the doctors today do not devise any diet for their patients and do nothing to find the underlying cause or how to prevent or cure the disease in the future. The advice by the doctors nowadays is just "management" of the disease, and for every health problem, whether minor or acute, they prescribe the modern drugs and medications which cause immense overall harm to the human body.

For example, if you have high blood pressure commonly known as hypertension, the doctor would prescribe diuretics that help to lower the pressure. But the side-effects of this medication include, but are not limited to, digestive disorders, kidney damage, erectile dysfunction, increase in LDL (bad cholesterol), loss of essential minerals like potassium that further leads to irregular heartbeat. The medication will not heal the problem of high blood pressure, it only helps to maintain normal levels with regular dosage. The drug would have to be taken life-long, and with time the dosage needs to be increased as the body gets used to it. As you continue taking it, the side-effects will gradually begin to manifest. Then you will be prescribed a new drug in addition to this for either digestive disorders, erectile dysfunction, irregular heartbeat, or to reduce LDL. Each new medication will have further side-effects of their own.

In general, with the increase in LDL (bad cholesterol) due to the blood pressure medication, the risk for heart attack and stroke is greatly enhanced. The drug to reduce LDL has its own side effects which include, but are not limited to, constipation, nausea, diarrhea, cramps, memory loss, and as per FDA warning – it elevates blood sugar levels leading to type II diabetes. Once you turn diabetic, the medication for that will have additional side effects, which include: weight gain, heart attack, heart failure, kidney failure, liver disease, and an increased risk of bladder cancer and thyroid tumors.

The circle of medications is extremely vicious, one drug leading to the other, then other, and another. Once you begin taking a drug to control blood pressure, the next in line would be a drug to control LDL, and then additional drugs for diabetes, liver disease, thyroid, irregular heartbeat etc.

The list is in fact endless, and eventually the combination of various drugs will lead to chronic kidney disease, which reduces kidney function over a period of time and eventually results in kidney failure of not just one, but both the kidneys. It is usually in the forties when most people begin having simple health issues, like high blood pressure, and then, they get on the bandwagon of medications. It would take a further 10 to 15 years of having a cocktail of various prescription drugs for other major issues to manifest. For example, liver disease, heart attack, heart failure, kidney failure, and the worst of all – cancer. The circle is indeed vicious and once a person gets stuck in it, he becomes a 'patient' whose body has fallen prey to these medications.

If you look at the official statistics, the situation is not only alarming, but catastrophic. Chronic kidney disease is rapidly increasing in people aged 60 and over, and has more than tripled in the last 15 years. As of April 2015 in the United States alone, there were over 123,000 patients on waitlist for organ transplants, out of which 101,622 were for kidney transplant alone. Over 3000 people are added to the organ transplant list every month, while a new name gets on the kidney list every 14 minutes. On an average, 21 people die every day due to lack of available organs and over 6000 every year who are on the waitlist. Where cancer is concerned, there were 14 million new cases and 8.2 million deaths worldwide in 2012 as per the World Health Organization. In the USA over 1.6 million new cases are expected in 2015 and over 600,000 deaths. It remains the second most common cause of death, accounting for 1 out of every 4 deaths.

According to the tenets of the Hippocratic Oath, as prevention is better than cure or rehabilitation, before any doctor even prescribes a blood pressure, or any other medication, he needs to first find out the reasons for the elevated levels. He should determine if the patient has any stress factors, whether he drinks enough water to keep the blood and body hydrated, his exercise routine, and if he is having too many processed or fried foods that harden the arteries and increase pressure on the heart. After finding out these essential details, he should first advise the patient to make lifestyle changes, which can easily bring the blood pressure down to normal levels. If the drug indeed has to be prescribed due to highly elevated levels, it should be for short-term only, and the doctor should clearly make the patient understand that.

It is also essential that the doctor shares with the patient the list of various side-effects and the increased risk of multiple health problems with continued use of the drug. This is how it should be, but sadly it is not, as doctors do take the Hippocratic Oath when graduating, but fail to implement it in their daily routines. While health problems and diseases continue to multiply at an astronomical pace, the sales of drugs and medications are at an all-time high. The overall revenue of the US Health Care Industry in 2014 exceeded USD 1.6 trillion. You can well imagine what the drug industry's revenue for the entire world must be.

Your health is in your hands, not in the hands of your doctor or anyone else. Of-course, if you are already on prescription drugs, it's imperative you discuss the information provided here and work closely with your doctor to gradually get away from them. When you begin a new way of life to go back to nature and heal your Self, regular monitoring and blood tests need to be done from time to time to determine the required level of reduction in the dosage of medications. There are many enlightened doctors who have already taken their patients on this path of recovery toward good health. If you are in your thirties or forties and minor health problems have just begun, it is advisable to look for such a doctor who'll not prescribe drugs, but help you with healthy natural alternatives.

My Mother was a staunch fan of modern drugs and medications, while my Father, an ardent crusader of natural cures. While battling a chronic headache for 46 years, she consumed an enormous amount of pain-killers and drugs, as she always wanted a quick relief and could not wait for the slower process of natural healing. Although, my Father kept giving her homeopathic medicines, but as she did not have any faith in them, they were not of much help. The headaches eventually disappeared when I introduced her to the Natural Water Therapy in 2002. The daily morning intake of 1.5 liters water healed her in a month, which modern medications could not for 46 years. Most people that I know are no different than my Mother. Everyone looks for an immediate solution to their health issues and do not have the patience to seek a permanent cure. As such, the modern health care system, which is in fact a disease-care system, does that job perfectly. As long you continue taking the prescribed drugs, the disease stays under control, but eventually leads to multiple health problems.

When my Father left Earth in the year 2000, it wasn't easy for my Mother to bear the great loss of his companionship. She stayed depressed for months and kept wondering why her life-partner had left her behind. The state of depression led to hypertension that elevated her blood pressure, and she began taking a prescribed medication to keep it under control. With continued use of that drug for 9 years, she frequently experienced digestive disorders – a common side-effect of blood pressure medication. Eventually, because of the drug or the digestive orders, she developed Ulcerative Colitis, a stomach disorder that cannot be healed by any modern drug or medication. Like all other medical conditions, once you are diagnosed with this, you'll be on permanent medication for life.

Ulcerative Colitis is an autoimmune disease, and is caused when the immune system begins attacking the colon. Due to this condition, the colon gets inflamed and develops ulcers, leading to digestive disorders with excessive bowel movement and bleeding. If functions of the immune system are restored and the digestive system is placed in order by natural methods, this disease can be permanently cured. Taking this approach I embarked upon a journey in 2009 to heal my Mother, with the help of Dr. James Brodsky, a well-known practicing Naturopath and Homeopath in Southern

California.

Our initial challenge was to get her off the blood pressure medication, as I believed that was the root cause of the problem. Dr. Brodsky advised me to get a digital blood pressure monitor and record her blood pressure six times a day. Her first reading was 205/105, and gradually with the help of natural supplements, like garlic pills and a complete diet and lifestyle change, which included, yoga, walking, acupressure, and Reiki, amazing results began to come forth. Her bowel movements became regular and the blood pressure dropped to 150/85 within a span of 2 months. She was taken off medications and some of her favorite foods, like dairy, beans, meats, wheat, tea, soda, and they were replaced with vitamin C enriched fresh organic fruits and steamed vegetables, lentils, Apple cider vinegar with honey, Aloe Vera juice, flax seeds etc. With this new diet and lifestyle change, she was completely healed from all the discomfort and pains associated with ulcerative colitis in 6 months, and within a year her blood pressure had dropped to a normal level of 125/80. She met the natural treatment with resistance initially but as she saw the benefits of the healthy lifestyle, soon she was convinced with the natural healing process.

My Mother's case is just an example of how even chronic autoimmune diseases can be healed and blood pressure can be brought down naturally. Dr. James Brodsky continues this great work of helping people get away from prescription drugs through this unique approach of diet and lifestyle changes, aided by natural supplements. He can be rightly called as per the words of Thomas A. Edison – "A doctor of the future who will give no medicine, but will interest his patients in the care of the human frame, in a proper diet, and in the cause and prevention of disease."

There is an interesting incident that took place while my Mother's treatment was on-going. Being a fan of the modern drugs and medications, as they provided quick relief to her health issues, she was unhappy with the natural way of treatment and lifestyle changes adopted to heal her. She did not like being taken off her favorite tea, milk, biscuits, meats and other foods, and insisted I take her to a senior medical doctor of Indian origin for a second opinion. When her condition had greatly improved after 2 months, I made an appointment with a doctor of her choice.

As we arrived at the clinic, the first thing the attending nurse checked was her blood pressure, which was 150/85. When the doctor saw this reading, he asked if she was taking any blood pressure medication. I told him, she was, but has now stopped. He was seemingly annoyed when he heard this and began explaining how important it was to take the medication, otherwise she could have a heart attack or stroke. I tried to explain that 2 months ago the reading was 205/105, and how with the lifestyle, diet change and natural supplements it had dropped down to 150/85. In addition, the other acute problem of ulcerative colitis was on the path to healing.

The doctor was in no mood to listen to my story and

insisted I continue with her blood pressure medication. He prescribed some blood and urine tests and gave an appointment to return after 2 weeks for the results. When we went back, all the tests were positive and everything seemed to be working right in my Mother's body. He was pleased to see the blood pressure reading had dropped down to 145/82, and advised to continue with the medication. Not to initiate any needless argument, I simply nodded, and didn't tell him that she was still off her blood pressure pill. As we had walked into his clinic that day, I was a little surprised to see his right arm in plaster from the elbow toward the palm. Although I felt a little reluctant to ask, I couldn't stop myself and enquired if he had had an accident. He replied kind of sheepishly, "Actually, last week I fell in the bathroom while taking shower and fractured my arm. I am diabetic and have hypertension, it seems my sugar must have dropped, as I felt dizzy and slipped in the bathtub."

I just could not believe this. A doctor who had studied and practiced medicine all his life was himself suffering from diabetes and hypertension. I thought, if he cannot heal himself, how can he possibly heal his patients? From that day onwards I began observing and having conversations with doctors I came across at any club meeting or social gathering. I found that the majority of them were unhealthy and had multiple health issues. Even their physiques were out of shape, and the most common excuse was that they had no time to exercise due to the demands of their medical profession. The drugs they usually prescribed for their patients are what they also took for their own health problems.

You live by the sword – you die by the sword. This is what scriptures strongly emphasize, and it relates to the law of sow and reap. If you kill or hurt someone with a sword or any other means, the same means will be used against you. If the doctors prescribe such drugs and medications that will not heal any disease, only control it with regular use, and ultimately result in multiple health issues leading to kidney failure, heart failure, cancer, and then a very painful death, how will they not be affected by this universal law of sow and reap? It's not as if the majority of them are doing this knowingly. Otherwise, they'll not take the same harmful drugs for their own health issues. When they go to medical schools to study medicine, this is what they are taught.

It's no secret – the drug industry controls and influences medical schools with money and grants. The students are taught how to use prescription drugs as the only alternative to every health ailment. In 2009, two hundred students at the highest rated Harvard Medical School demanded an end to the drug industry's influence in the classroom. In 2008, the industry had contributed more than USD 11 million to Harvard for research and education. At the same time 1600 of their professors admitted they had a family member with ties to drug companies, which could have influenced their teaching and research. Harvard school received the lowest possible 'F' grade on how well they monitored and controlled drug industry money. It was also revealed in the New York Times, a professor at Harvard was a paid consultant to 10 drug companies, and he taught and promoted the benefits of drugs, while going as far as to belittle a student who dared to ask about the possible side-effects.

If this kind of thing is happening at Harvard, you can well imagine the state of affairs at other medical schools worldwide. Although, the American Medical Student Association (AMSA) is actively pursuing to change the system of education to teach students true healing practices, instead of solely relying on drugs that do not heal. It is now mandatory for Harvard professors to disclose in the classrooms their interests and ties with the drug industry. It will take a long time for real change to come, as the drug companies are doing all they can to not only sustain, but also increase their sales. That is why in the USA alone, they spend over USD 16 billion every year to influence doctors.

Mahatma Gandhi, the legendary freedom fighter, once said, "Be the change you wish to see in the world. There is a sufficiency in the world for man's need, but not for man's greed. It is health that is real wealth and not pieces of gold and silver." How true and significant these words are in today's world, where the drug industry, the food industry, our health and most importantly our wellbeing is concerned. There is virtually nothing you can do to change the greed of the drug industry, chemicals and genetically modified food industry, or the way of education at medical schools. But there's something extremely significant only you can do, and that is, change yourself. As spiritual beings in human bodies, our greatness does not lie so much in being able to change the world, but in being able to change ourselves. It is our individual change that will bring the greatest benefit not only to us, but the entire world. One less unhealthy being will be a boon to society and an inspiration to countless others.

In Chapter 2, a lot of light was thrown on the Law of Change, and how successfully Senator Barack Obama used it to become the first African-American President of the most powerful nation in the world. It's all about change you believe in – And yes, you too can use this law to become the President of the most powerful and magical human body in the entire universe. Upon taking office every President has to take this Oath: "I do solemnly swear that I will faithfully execute the office of President of the United States, and will to the best of my ability, preserve, protect and defend the constitution of the United States."

In reality, the human body is no different than a nation. In a nation millions or billions of people live, while in the human body, trillions of cells live. The world population in 2015 was 7.3 billion, while the human body has a population of 37.2 trillion cells. If there is a constitution that has been made for a nation and the President has to take an Oath upon taking office to preserve, protect and defend it, the human body has its own constitution as well. As a matter of fact, the United States constitution is the oldest in the world and has played a major role in limiting government and creating freedom. One of its most important purposes was to protect the rights of life, liberty, and the pursuit of happiness.

The human body's constitution created by the Creator

or Nature is no doubt the oldest of all constitutions. It was actually made to limit disease and create freedom from sickness, and protect the rights of life and liberty of all the cells and organs in the pursuit of real happiness of the Spirit living inside. Each part or organ of the constitution was created in a unique manner, not only to self-heal, but also re-create itself. When President Obama took Office, there was a great deal of economic mess due to the policies of the previous government and the nation was in acute financial crisis. Unlike the human body, a nation cannot self-heal and bail itself out of an economic mess or solve any financial crisis. So he had to form a number of teams and policies to bring things back in order. The goals he made to restore the economic health of the nation have taken almost 7 years to manifest.

You are no different than the President of any nation. This human body is your nation, and the various organs and cells are the people who voted you into Office to look after their well-being. The only issue is – you have forgotten who you are and have allowed negative elements to invade your sovereign territory. By leading an unhealthy lifestyle and giving easy access to foods laden with pesticides and genetically modified organisms to enter your kingdom and create disease, and then bombarding your organs and cells with nuclear-like prescription drugs to contain the damage – you've lost track of your presidential duties. It's high time you took the oath to preserve, protect, and defend your body's constitution to the best of your abilities.

On the morning of September 11, 2001, four passenger planes from the airports of East Coast heading to California were hijacked by 19 Al-Qaeda terrorists. Two of them were crashed into the twin towers of the World Trade Center in New York. Within an hour and 42 minutes both 110 storied towers collapsed, while debris and resulting fires led to the collapse of many other adjoining buildings, including the 47 storied World Trade Center. The attacks claimed the lives of 2996 people and caused over USD 10 billion in property damage and USD 3 trillion in overall costs. This was the deadliest incident for firefighters and law enforcement officers in the history of United States, and 415 of them lost their lives.

Imagine, if after 9/11, President Bush had opened borders and airports to allow free access for terrorists to enter and cause more harm and destruction? Obviously, it would be insane to even think of such a situation. Rather, he did what was ethical by launching a war on terror to eradicate the root cause and strengthen the security network to prevent any further attacks. Many other nations took note of this to strengthen their own security networks, and expanded the powers of law enforcement agencies to prevent such attacks. Eventually, the leader who claimed responsibility for these attacks, Osama Bin Laden, was tracked in Pakistan 10 years later and brought down by the U.S. military forces in May 2011.

Foods laden with pesticides, growth hormones and genetically modified organisms, and prescription drugs, are no different from these terrorists who hijacked the planes and crashed them into the twin towers. The only difference between the two is – While the damage inflicted by those terrorists was immediate and the buildings were destroyed within a short span of time, whereas, the destruction from such foods and drugs on the human bodies is gradual. The debris from the twin towers led to the collapse of many adjoining buildings. In a similar fashion, the debris from our lifestyle and wrong food choices cause immense damage to people who are close to us. Those attacks by the terrorists resulted into the deaths of 2996 people, while the death rate from the continuous attacks on the human bodies by terrorists in the form of harmful foods and drugs is staggering. From cancer alone, there were over 8 million deaths worldwide in 2012. Every year 14 million new cases are being reported and thousands die due to lack of available organs.

As you are the President and your Body is the nation, when will you do what President Bush did after 9/11? Your Body is in a continuous mode of attack by terrorists or toxins that generate from an unhealthy lifestyle, harmful foods, and prescription drugs. They are destroying and killing millions of cells non-stop. So when will you launch a war against them to eradicate the root cause and prevent further attacks? Timing is of great importance and a critical factor in strengthening the security network, which is your immune system, to begin the process of safeguarding the organs and millions of cells living inside your Body. Just as Osama Bin Laden was the leader of the terrorists, there is a leader within you – called 'Procrastination', which not only protects, but also helps in ample multiplication of the terrorist network of toxins.

While it took 10 years and billions of dollars for the American forces to find Bin Laden and bring him down, for you, a simple 'To-Do List' can easily eliminate procrastination and protect your body. As explained in Chapter 2, once you have a list in front of you highlighting the required daily tasks to restore your health, and a resolve to do today what others may leave for tomorrow, and do now, what others may leave for later – you will turn into an Action-taker, and not a procrastinator. It is essential to prepare your Health Restoration To-do List with proper care and attention. Each individual's needs and goals are different, but in general, the list should clearly spell out all the required tasks. You may need to go through this book once again, but in a nutshell, the elements to be taken into consideration should include: A daily exercise plan, intake of sufficient water to keep your body and blood hydrated, fresh organic raw vegetables and fruits, Apple cider vinegar, honey, cinnamon, and ginger drink, weekly fasts, and to avoid all GMO foods.

To begin your journey and Go Back to Nature, it is imperative you learn how to love your Self. You simply cannot love anyone else, even God, if you don't love your Self. I know many people who are very religious, and will not leave home or begin any work assignment before getting through with their morning ritual of prayers and meditation.

They believe in praying and offering thanks to God, before anything else, as an expression of their love and gratitude toward the unknown supreme creator of the universe. Although, they may spend a good amount of time every morning to perform these rituals without fail, but will hardly have any time for taking care of the Body they live in.

Scriptures are full of quotes that are more like parables, and they point toward the real truth about the human body and God in very simple terms. Many people complain, it is difficult to understand the meaning of such words. But I fail to understand what is so difficult to understand? When the scriptures say: The Human Body is the Temple of God and the Kingdom of God is within you – the meaning is crystal clear. In an easy and simple language, the body in which we live has been termed as the temple, and the kingdom is inside of it. Our flesh, organs, and trillions of cells – Are they not a part of that very temple and kingdom? When you begin to love your Self, you will have to love these cells and organs, as they are an integral part of you. To love them means – to take care of them, and for that, you'll have to reserve some time out of your busy schedule.

I am not religious as other people may be, but I too, will not leave home or begin any work assignment before I am through with the morning rituals of taking care of my body. I don't believe in sitting with folded hands to pray and thank our Creator, but rather, use the same hands to do the required work to keep his temple and kingdom clean, pure, and healthy. I term these daily rituals as Body-worship, and they include: Drinking 1.5 liters water to flush out all the toxins and poisons, breathing exercises, acupressure, aerobics, Reiki/chakras/energy balancing, and yoga/strength training exercises. If at times I have to leave home early, I simply wake up an hour or two sooner, but not leave without completing this worship. Why? Because – I love myself and it's my foremost duty before anything else, to love and care for the body I live in.

Being a religious person if you pray every morning, there's no problem in that. I know such prayers give people hope and build their faith, which does have a positive impact on their lives. There is basically no right or wrong way as it's an individual choice, but under no circumstances should care for the body be neglected. If you consider the daily prayers and worship important, then the Body-worship is equally important. How can you truly demonstrate your love for God and what greater gratitude can you possibly offer, than to care for his most wondrous creation – the human body?

If you are a parent and your children act in a similar manner – how would you feel? A mother and father are in actual reality – Gods on Earth for a child, as they're directly responsible for his birth and well-being. Nobody has seen the other God, but these Gods are visible on Earth in everyone's life. Imagine, if before leaving home they sit down in front of you and go through the same rituals of praying, seeking your blessings, and requesting what they need. I am certain you would endeavor to fulfil their requirements to the best of your abilities. But on the other hand, they abuse their physical bodies during the day with wrong foods, drinks, and a lack of exercise. Then, they keep falling sick frequently, their physiques get out of shape and health problems continue to multiply. Every now and then you have to escort them to a doctor, who would prescribe harmful drugs that would not heal the problem, but cause more disease.

Would such a scenario make you happy? The answer is quite obvious – no parent will be pleased with such a situation. No one knows the value of a child's body more than a mother. She nurtures that body in her womb for 9 months, takes care of her diet by consuming only healthy foods during pregnancy, and eventually goes through intense labor pains to breathe life into it. If the child begins to abuse and harm that very body, there would be no greater pain for her to bear. She would prefer any day that the child cares for the body instead of wasting time in worshipping her. Her most precious gift is that wondrous body, and the only way the child can truly express thanks, is by taking care of it. And if the child genuinely loves her, how can he not take care of this priceless gift?

The situation with God is no different. I am sure he does not need our praise or worship, and would be most happy if we took care of the amazing body he has gifted us. Ultimately, it's all about love and loving ourselves, as that is the energy which holds and binds the entire universe and creation together. What we term as God is the same energy of love, and we are the byproducts of that very love. When you come to realize your true identity – The Spirit inside a human body – you'll find the same love running in every vein, organ and cell. It is this heavenly, unconditional love that pervades the universe and is the true source of all creation. I know I am love – pure unconditional love, that's all that I am, was, or ever will be – and so is each one of you. The eternal fabric that has created me, you, and everyone else, including every single thing in the universe, is nothing but pure unconditional love.

People often say – love never dies, but then, we see numerous love relationships turning sour and dying all the time. It all begins from you. If you are not able to love your Self, how can you love anybody else? If due to your own unhealthy relationship with your body, the cells and organs are decaying and gradually moving toward death, the situation will be no different with all outer relationships you share with people. When the scriptures emphasize – love your neighbor as yourself, the same principle of loving your Self first is being reinforced.

How we understand God, religion, and love is actually what has created divisions and made our world so complicated, fearful, and the reason behind all the conflicts, wars, terrorism, greed, and disease. From infancy a child is taught to be fearful with such words – do not touch this, do not go there, or do not eat this. The list of don'ts is virtually absolute, and there's no greater negative than fear that is gradually placed in a child's mind. Each one of us is born free, because the Spirit does not know what fear is. When we are little children, the Spirit is in supreme control, until the mind takes over with constant feeding of the fear factor into our psyche by parents, society, and the education system.

As we turn into adults, fear takes on greater forms that may turn monstrous if left unchecked. There could be fear of not measuring up to your parents, teachers, or society's expectations, which may keep your self-esteem low. Fear of failure can keep you miles away from the ladder of success. While, the fear of falling sick and being diagnosed with a dangerous condition like cancer, can actually help and bring that into manifestation. The scriptures have so rightly said: What you fear, will come upon you. A modern interpretation of the word FEAR describes it as: False Evidence Appearing Real.

The greatest of all fears that humankind is infested with, is the fear of death. If you look at the world statistics, there are 56 million deaths every year, which sums up to a daily death rate of 153,000. When so many people are dying every day it would be hard not to be afraid of death, but in reality, this is just – False Evidence Appearing Real. As a matter of fact, it's the bodies that are dying, not the Spirits. You can understand this truth today and gain freedom from the fear of dying, or you can wait for several lifetimes, it's all up to you. But until you gain freedom from death, you simply cannot live life as it is meant to be lived.

Many people have gone through Near Death Experiences, when their Spirit left the body while they were in a coma or lying unconscious in a hospital. It was during that phase that they realized who they really were, their true capabilities and powers, purpose on Earth, and the reality of the universe. Anita Moorjani, in her best-selling book, 'Dying To Be Me', shares such an extraordinary experience and her journey from cancer to near death, to true healing. While her organs were shutting down and the body was in a state of coma, she found herself to be in a different world altogether, in a state of awareness where no death or physical time existed. Not only was she able to discover the reasons for the cancer that had ravaged her body, she also came to know that her body would heal once she returned back into it.

This is a must-read book in which Anita beautifully narrates her life story, the circumstances that led to cancer, her journey out of her body, and the magical disappearance of the disease, which was nothing short of a miracle in medical terms. She not only healed, but also realized there was nothing like death, as that was just a word related to the physical body. She was, in reality, the soul which never dies, and was connected to all other souls in the universe. This was in actuality the energy or essence of pure unconditional love that people term as God, and she was an eternal part of it all. The only thing that had kept her from becoming aware of her true identity was the mind with all its deep-rooted fears and childhood conditioning. When she was out of her body, the mind got out of the way, and it was then she discovered her true greatness and purpose on Earth.

The journey of Anita Moorjani can simply be described as a journey into death, and then returning back as a 'Born Again' being. She died of all the unreal elements she thought were real. She was neither her body, nor her fears, or mind, or her doubts, but in reality, she was a divine essence of pure consciousness and unconditional love. When she began living with that awareness, fear got out of the way, and the cancer was eliminated with her self-belief and unconditional love for herself. At the same time, she realized her true purpose on earth, a part of which was sharing the story of her near death experience and magical healing with the entire world, so others could learn and benefit from it.

This is the true state of being Born Again that many world religions talk about. It's not about physical death, but the death of all the unreal factors and fears that surround us, and a realization of our true identity and purpose in life. Only when you get the mind out of the way – will you know the truth about your Self. You are not the body that will die one day. You are love – pure unconditional love, that's all you are, were, or ever will be. The entire creation is made up of the same love, and all you need to do is to be what you truly are. To be and demonstrate the power of true unconditional love, you'll have to first love your Self and care for the physical body you live in. If you cannot do that, there is no possibility of fulfilling your journey and mission on Earth.

Michael Jackson and Steve Jobs were two immensely gifted individuals who gave a lot to the world through their unique talents, but had to leave at an early age due to health problems. In the end no amount of wealth could save their bodies from death. Michael had even sung a beautiful song on healing, in which he emphasized that we should heal the world and make it a better place for you and me and the entire human race by taking care of the living. But sadly, he wasn't able to take care of his own living body and departed at age 51. He was due to perform a series of concerts in London from July 2009 to March 2010, but left without fulfilling one of his deepest desires of staging a comeback in the music world.

Steve Jobs was the co-founder of Apple, and his passion for perfection and creative drive revolutionized personal computers, cellphones, music, animated movies, and digital publishing. During his lifetime he gained immense recognition and wealth, but all that became meaningless in the face of an early death at age 56, due to cancer. It is said, he once mentioned that you could employ people to work and earn money for you, but you cannot employ anyone to bear your sickness, and it was important to take care of your health to avoid disease and an untimely death.

Good health is indeed the greatest wealth anyone can ever acquire, so is this not what we all should seek? Had Michael Jackson and Steve Jobs invested a little of their time into seeking this kind of wealth, they could have continued their journey for many more years and inspired millions with their steadfast and creative dedication to the work they were so passionate about. Imagine, how many more amazing gadgets Steve Jobs could have created, and the joy and entertainment Michael Jackson may have provided with his songs and music, had they lived for another 50 years. They could have achieved that, if a little more care had been provided to the bodies they lived in, and not allowed toxins from foods, drinks, drugs and medications to ravage them.

Would you allow a bunch of thieves to enter your home and live with you under the same roof to rob you daily of your joy and possessions? I am certain no one would ever do that. Toxins and poisons from unhealthy foods are no less than thieves, as they develop sickness and disease inside your body and rob you of your joy and possessions by damaging your cells and organs. The prescription drugs and medications do not help to resolve the actual issues, as any drug that does not heal but creates more disease cannot help the body to eliminate toxins. A thief may rob or shoot you with a gun and cause instant death without any prolonged suffering or pain, whereas the unhealthy foods and drugs you consume will gradually shoot toxicity into your body, which will lead to a slow painful death with immense suffering. If you will not invite a bunch of thieves to enter your home, then how can you willingly allow the entry of such harmful toxins and poisons into your body?

There is an unknown place called 'Heaven'. Nobody has ever been there or physically witnessed what it looks like, but everyone wants to go there once their journey on Earth is over. People believe this is a place where there will be total bliss and freedom from all pain, sufferings, and struggles. The scriptures of all world religions talk about this heaven and show the way to get there. The millions of people worldwide who flock to religious abodes, or pray in their homes and follow a fixed set of rules, have one thing in common. They all seek an entry into this unknown Heaven.

In sharp contrast to Heaven, there's a second unknown place called 'Hell'. Nobody has ever been there either, or physically witnessed what it looks like, but no-one wants to go there once their journey on earth is over. People believe this is a place where there will be absolute pain and suffering, and all the inhabitants will burn in the raging fires controlled by Satan and his demons. The scriptures of all world religions also talk about this Hell and show the way to not get there.

In reality, both Heaven and Hell are not in any far away or distant land. As a matter of fact, they're both right here and are an integral part of the physical body you live in. If your health is in order, the body in a continuous state of regeneration and every organ is functioning in the most optimum manner – you'll experience a state of bliss. When there is no sickness or disease, you will have absolute freedom from the related pains, stress, and suffering. That will be your living Heaven. On the other hand, if your health is not in order, the body in a continuous state of degeneration and organs are malfunctioning or dying with cancer and disease – you'll experience a state of misery. When you are surrounded with sickness and disease, dangerous drugs and medications that provide no permanent healing – you will find yourself imprisoned in a body full of pains, stress, and suffering. That will be your living Hell.

You are the Spirit inside a human body – let there be no doubt in your mind about this truth and reality, and it's your personal choice to be in Heaven or Hell. It doesn't matter if you've lived in ignorance of your true personality till now, the moment you get the mind out of the way – you will begin to see glimpses of who you really are. You don't need to go through a Near Death Experience to be Born Again and make radical changes to your life – you can do it right now. All you need is a subtle shift to transfer the thought and decision making powers from the mind to the heart. It won't be an easy process, but is not that difficult either. The mind will not easily relinquish its control over you, but the moment you make the health of your body the first priority and begin caring for it, the power of the Spirit will gradually rise.

The state of your good health will not only go a long way to ensure your comfort and bliss, it will also generate phenomenal success in all your endeavors and missions, which you can truly enjoy for a great number of years. When one person lights the candle of this kind of self-love to attain optimum health, many other candles will be lit, from one home to the neighborhood, from the neighborhood to the city, from the city to the nation, and ultimately to the entire world. The spellbinding light of these candles will eventually awaken all the Spirits imprisoned in unhealthy, sick, and diseased bodies, and bring in a new world order – where peace, love, and good health will reign supreme, and signal the end of wars, terrorism, greed, poverty, unhealthy foods, and poisonous drugs.

You can be that one revolutionary Spirit to light such a candle of self-love and initiate the journey of Going Back to Nature to renew your body and heal your Self, and then, experience true Heaven on Earth. There is no other way, but to become the Change you want to see in the world and earn your place in that Heaven. If you believe the world and the people out there are not fair and have not treated you well – you become fair to your inner world and begin treating your very own organs and cells in the way you would expect others to treat you. If you believe there are too many senseless wars and needless corruption in the world – you better take care of your own internal wars and save your body from corrupted organs and cells. Change – you can believe in. Yes – you can be the change you believe in and attain the kind of magical success you may have never ever dreamt of.

And your time to begin, starts NOW!

The Difference between yourself and your 'Self'

My daughter, Alipt Sanam Hari, while editing this Book asked me the difference between yourself and your 'Self'. I thought many of you might ask the same question, so I am sharing with you the explanation I gave her.

When you are deeply attached to your external identity, and your reference point is – I am this or that, or I am the body, that is the 'yourself' you become attached to. Your and Self are two separate words, and the confusion arises from their attachment. In actual reality, 'Self' is the highest level of consciousness or the seat of personal awareness of who you truly are, beyond the realms of the ordinary sense-world.

When I write, know your Self, I've knowingly created a space between your and self to signify the gap that exists between the two. It is this gap that can make you more mindful of the identity of the Self, which is the true source of our existence and infinite power. In your journey of self-discovery, it is only when the mind realizes the existence of the Self, that it will cease projecting fears, worries, and anxieties.

The attachment to our external identity is very similar to our attachment to Time. The Self is timeless, and so is the Universe, which signifies there is no end or death of either.

We created the physical time by dividing into segments one rotation of the earth and one orbit of the sun. While this Time does have its own use and purpose in the external time-bound existence that we have got associated with, it has created profound confusion in the mind as we have become enslaved to this ideology.

It is important to separate the two – The time-bound and the timeless, just like, your and Self to gain freedom from the entrenched shackles of time-bound existence, attain self-mastery to salvage our lost heritage and once again become a Supreme Master of your Self.

A Final Note

I would love to hear from you

Thank you for taking this journey with me of going back to Nature and healing your Self. As you may have realized that Knowledge turns into Wisdom only when practically applied. I truly hope you will make an effort to do that and discover your true identity to fulfil the purpose of your eternal existence in this beautiful Universe, with a sense of heavenly love, joy and bliss.

Love is the basic essence of our being, and when it flows out freely without any barriers, it brings in a kind of intoxication that cannot be matched by any drug or alcohol. It is our birthright to be in such a joyful and blissful state in each and every moment of our lives. When our Body is perfectly attuned to the laws of Nature, and all the cells and organs are in a state of regeneration, we can experience that state known as – Heaven on Earth.

This Book is simply a guide to help you reach there. It is said: Angels live in Heaven and are blessed with supernatural powers to perform miracles. You are no less than any Heavenly Angel and truly possess the same kind of powers. These powers are simply hidden behind the veils of ignorance that surround your body and mind. Your treasure is truly where your heart is. Your only job is to properly care for the Body that houses that treasure and experience the richness of your Being.

You can email me any questions or queries you may have at any time or connect with me on Facebook. I would love to hear from you.

Love is all that I am, all that I have, and all that I can give you. And I have it in abundance, because the more I give – the more I receive back. In fact, my coffers are full and keep overflowing endlessly.

Gurdip Hari

Email: Love@Healthisultimatewealth.com

My Dream School

As highlighted in Chapter 4, I have personally taken the initiative to build such Creative Schools in Ghana as per the blue-print on the adjoining page. Education will be imparted from Kindergarten to High school and 25 percent seats will be reserved for under-privileged children, who will have access to free education.

The first school is now under construction at Madina in Accra, and should be ready to commence operations in 2018. Besides providing the best available education, the school will have finer arts facilities to include classes in modern and traditional music, singing, painting, nutrition, health, drama, speech, and dancing. It will be equipped with studios for visual and performing arts, and have facilities for tennis, basketball, hockey, soccer, and athletics. Every child has a unique in-born talent, generosity and love in the heart. True education means to help them discover these virtues in an atmosphere of joy and fun with activities that engage all their five sense modalities. The focus will be to teach and create a conducive environment that fosters creative thought and action, and to hone their inherent talents to optimize their best potential. For example, if a child is good at singing, besides providing the best available education, the primary focus would be to whet the child's vocal skills to become a good singer. Likewise, if someone is good in sports, drama, accounting or business, they will be trained and educated to become professionals in those spheres.

Healthy Mind International
"A School of the Future –
For the Children of Today"

What are people saying about this Book

"Body and Mind Consciousness"

The ideas and principles espoused by Gurdip Hari in the main are consistent with recognized knowledge relevant to our very existence on earth. The need to keep our bodies clean have long been appreciated by humankind and has formed the basis of any health preventive initiative of medicine. Any physician that manages a patient with a chronic health condition without emphasizing on the importance of lifestyle adjustments (i.e., healthy/appropriate diet and exercise) is bound to achieve little. The exposition on GMO seeds is very informative and revealing, and buttresses the need for serious debate and appropriate legislation by respective governments to address the GMO quagmire. The fables, illustrations and analogies presented in the book are relevant and make interesting reading. Any open minded and information seeking person will feel motivated to make the necessary life changes after reading the book. It's all about body and mind consciousness to put your life and health in order.

Dr. David Nortey
Family Physician & Head of Polyclinic, Korle Bu
Teaching Hospital, Accra, Ghana

"Truly – An Eye-opener"

This Book is truly 'An Eye-opener" to help you discover your true identity and heal the body you live in. To find real everlasting success, the only way is to return to the tried and tested ways in line with the eternal laws of the universe. This is not just a book to read and forget. If you would like to bring real 'Change' into your life, family, and the world around you, practical application will be required to implement the knowledge it contains and see the results that come forth. Procrastination is one common habit that most people have, which prevents them from laying hands on abundance and success in their work and relationships. I believe, it all begins with your health, and that is mainly dependant upon regular exercise and eating the right foods.

Gurdip Hari uses facts, eternal truths, and beautiful fables not only to bring the reality of our existence from darkness to light, but also shows the way how to change our lifestyle by getting rid of 'Procrastination' with personal life examples that have helped him to find all-round success in life.

Yanni Maniates – Author of best-selling #1 on Amazon kindle "Magical Keys to Self-Mastery" and "When You Remember Who You Are; You Forget Who You Weren't"

http://www.insideoutjourneys.com

"A Wake-up Call"

Viewing the seven wonders of the world is a dream for all of us. Gurdip Hari, through this book has gone a step further and introduced us to the seven wonders of ultimate health – Daily exercise plan, Intake of sufficient water, Fresh organic vegetables and fruits, Apple cider vinegar and honey drink, Weekly fasts, Eliminating procrastination – And above all, loving the most wonderful and amazing wonder of the universe – our human body.

Besides being a treasure house of how to enjoy superb health and find success in your work and relationships, this book is a wake-up call from our slumber to the horrifying truth of GMO foods, pesticides and prescription drugs slowly leading us to disease, pain, suffering and eventually obliteration. Gurdip Hari takes you through an amazing journey of 'Self discovery', and if you can truly follow his guidelines, it will generate into a phenomenal service to the environment, humanity, and all living beings – including 'You'.

Inderpreet Sandhu
Chandigarh, India

"An Amazing Revelation"

I have personally known the author for a number of years. I first met him through the service organization of Rotary International. I often remember a talk he gave to the Rotary Club of South Gate in which the image is still engraved in me of the importance of cleaning out the church or temple after a service attended by many people. As he has related, the body is the temple of the spirit. For many years, with a glimmer in his eye and a calming smile he would mention how his present book was coming along. "Go Back to Nature & Heal your Self" demonstrates the relentless research towards a healthy mind, spirit, and body the author has attained. I find that Gurdip Hari is able to energize the mind to motivate and encourage a change in habits for a healthier body. It is impressionable how unselfish he is with this information and readily shares it with the world.

Dental and health organizations such as the Academy for Oral Systemic Health, American Dental Association, California Dental Association, and Mayo Clinic, to mention a few, have mentioned that there are correlating links between the bacteria in the mouth and heart disease, high blood pressure, stroke, rheumatoid arthritis and premature death. A study out of Harvard concluded that gum disease (caused by bacteria) can increase pancreatic and kidney cancer. As a dentist of over 30 years in private practice, we put great effort into educating patients on the importance of oral health since bacteria that lives in the mouth can circulate into the blood stream and connect with different organs in the body. We emphasize daily brushing and flossing throughout the day since bacteria are always present and multiplying. By keeping the bacterial count down, we can begin to attain good oral health. Regularly scheduled "cleanings" with a dental hygienist or dentist are necessary to remove bacterial plaque and calcified deposits that contain toxins (waste products). The author goes into great depth on the importance of removing toxins from the body, and we instruct our patients to remove bacteria from the mouth that would greatly help in removing the overall toxicity.

This book is truly 'An Amazing Revelation' to direct us on to the path of attaining optimum health, vitality, and success in life.

Dr. Jose Flores, Downey, CA, USA

"Absolutely Unique and Marvelous"

There are many books on health and healing, but this is absolutely unique and marvelous as Gurdip Hari shares his personal journey to good health, depicting an interchange between ancient philosophy, reason and nature. Anyone can benefit from his tried and tested ways of life.

Dr. Ram Chellaram, Houston, Texas, USA

" A Powerful Preventive Tool"

There is no denying that we are huge followers of Gurdip Hari's writings. His previous book "Mental, Physical and Spiritual Health" is our bible of sorts, our 'go-to' bedside book that we refer to all the time, for the practical knowledge and highly effective tried and tested way of life and remedies that it carries. This book 'Go Back to Nature & Heal your Self' delves deeper and further into wellness, powerful preventive tools, natural cures and viable lifestyle changes. God's own guinea pig, as he calls himself, what's remarkable about his writing and insights is that he doesn't profess, rather encourages you to benefit from information that he has culled from first hand experience and research over the years.

Sandeep and Adarsh Brar, Gurgaon, India

"Health and Longevity"

To nourish your soul, health and longevity, this book is highly recommended!

Khushwant Singh, Chandigarh, India
Author of "Maharaja in Denims" and "Turbaned Tornado"

"A Compelling Blueprint for Change"

Life is the greatest gift of God to us. What we do with our lives and our health is our fundamental responsibility.

In this new book, "Go Back To Nature & Heal your Self," award winning author Gurdip Hari traces certain fundamental lifestyle changes over the past decades and their impact on the quality of our lives today. He examines negative trends in notable areas like family, marriage, education, communication, agriculture and medicine. He then goes on to offer a compelling blueprint for changing your worldview, your attitude and your life.

Readers will find this book very down-to-earth and easy to grasp. If you want to know yourself, understand your journey and live life to the full, take time to read and practice the thoughts and truths shared in this book by our friend, Gurdip Hari.

Albert & Comfort Ocran
Authors & Executive Coaches
Accra, Ghana

"A Priceless Gem"

Gurdip Hari has presented in this book a wealth of wisdom attained through a lifetime of practical applications of the knowledge that came his way. I am that cousin he mentions who gave him the advice on how to succeed or fail in life, on the first day of his first job, 40 years ago. It makes me ecstatic to know how profoundly he made practical application of that and attained immense success in every area of his life. Not only did he run the businesses he worked for as if he was the owner, he has run his own life in the same manner and become a 'Master of his Destiny'.

Health is certainly our greatest Wealth, and this book is a priceless gem with a storehouse of knowledge about universal laws, the human body, and tried and tested techniques on how to improve your health, and attain success in work and relationships. The importance of exercise, diet, fasting, raw vegetables, and the danger of GMO foods has been very well explained.

The advice I gave him 40 years ago, I've given to many, but he is the only one who made practical application and reaped the benefits. This book is a gift to mankind as it contains his success secrets. Anyone can make practical application of this timeless knowledge and attain the same kind of success.

Raj Dhaliwal,
Downey, CA, USA

"Your Monthly Health To-Do List"

"Your Monthly Health To-Do List"

"Your Monthly Health To-Do List"

"Your Monthly Health To-Do List"

"Your Monthly Health To-Do List"

"Your Monthly Health To-Do List"

"Your Monthly Health To-Do List"

"Your Monthly Health To-Do List"

"Your Monthly Health To-Do List"

"Your Monthly Health To-Do List"

"Your Monthly Health To-Do List"

"Your Monthly Health To-Do List"

"Your Monthly Health To-Do List"